Life

WORKBOOK | PRE-INTERMEDIATE

JOHN HUGHES

Australia · Brazil · Mexico · Singapore · United Kingdom · United States

NATIONAL GEOGRAPHIC
L E A R N I N G

Life Pre-intermediate Workbook
John Hughes

Vice President, Editorial Director:
John McHugh

Executive Editor: Sian Mavor

Publishing Consultant: Karen Spiller

Development Editor: Clare Shaw

Contributing Writer: Nick Kenny
(IELTS practice test)

Editorial Manager: Claire Merchant

Head of Strategic Marketing ELT:
Charlotte Ellis

Senior Content Project Manager:
Nick Ventullo

Manufacturing Manager: Eyvett Davis

Senior IP Analyst: Ashley Maynard

Senior IP Project Manager: Michelle
McKenna

Cover: Lisa Trager

Text design: Vasiliki Christoforidou

Compositor: Lumina Datamatics

Audio: Prolingua Productions and Tom Dick
and Debbie Productions Ltd

DVD: Tom Dick and Debbie Productions Ltd

For product information and technology assistance, contact us at
Cengage Learning Customer & Sales Support, cengage.com/contact
For permission to use material from this text or product,
submit all requests online at **cengage.com/permissions**
Further permissions questions can be emailed to
permissionrequest@cengage.com

ISBN: 978-1-337-28586-5

National Geographic Learning
Cheriton House, North Way, Andover, Hampshire, SP10 5BE
United Kingdom

National Geographic Learning, a Cengage Learning Company, has a mission to bring the world to the classroom and the classroom to life. With our English language programs, students learn about their world by experiencing it. Through our partnerships with National Geographic and TED Talks, they develop the language and skills they need to be successful global citizens and leaders.

Locate your local office at **international.cengage.com/region**

Visit National Geographic Learning online at **NGL.Cengage.com/ELT**
Visit our corporate website at **www.cengage.com**

Credits
Although every effort has been made to contact copyright holders before publication, this has not always been possible. If notified, the publisher will undertake to rectify any errors or omissions at the earliest opportunity.

Text: p4 source: 'Global Health Crusader', by Keith Bellows, http://travel.nationalgeographic.com/travel/traveler-magazine/one-on-one/global-health-crusader/; p6 source: 'Community health', http://ngm.nationalgeographic.com/2008/12/community-doctors/rosenberg-text; p8 source: 'The Best Things in Life Aren't Things' 28/10/2010", http://blogs.nationalgeographic.com/blogs/news/chiefeditor/2010/10/the-best-things-in-life-arent.html; p12 source: http://ngadventure.typepad.com/blog/2010/07/interview-allstar-paddleboarder-jamie-mitchell-wins-.html?cid=6a00e55031d3a388340133f2b5d443970b; p15 source: http://ngadventure.typepad.com/blog/freeskiier-kristi-leskinen-is-a-superstar-officially.html; p16 source: http://ngadventure.typepad.com/blog/2010/11/interview-swed-annelie-pompe-on-snaring-new-free-diving-record-.html#more; p20 source: 'How to Green Your Transportation Choices', by Jeannette Belliveau, Demand Media, http://greenliving.nationalgeographic.com/green-transportation-choices-2478.html; p22 source: 'Camel Contest – isn't she lovely?' by Matthew Teague, Nat Geo magazine, August 2009, page 117-125 onwards. http://ngm.nationalgeographic.com/2009/08/camel-contest/teague-text/1; p23 source: "transport data", http://www.pewresearch.org/fact-tank/2015/04/16/car-bike-or-motorcycle-depends-on-where-you-live/; p24 source: 'the Golden Quadrilateral', Nat Geo 2008 Oct, pg 82-83. pp28–29 source: http://channel.nationalgeographic.com/series/dangerous-encounters/all/Photos#tab-Photos/0 and Erik Ronningsbakken. Found on http://animals.nationalgeographic.com/animals/wild/shows-dangerous-encounters/; p30 source: 'The 10 best survival stories', by Ed Douglas, 17 October, 2010, http://www.guardian.co.uk/culture/gallery/2010/oct/17/ten-best-survival-stories; p37 source: http://greenliving.nationalgeographic.com/household-items-commonly-reuse-3248.html; p38 source: 'Frequency of Recycling Materials', http://environment.nationalgeographic.com/environment/greendex/2009-survey/. Found on http://images.nationalgeographic.com/wpf/media-live/file/GS_NGS_Full_Report_May09-cb1274128119.pdf, p.246; pp38–39 source: http://www.ecofriendlyhouses.net/, and photo from http://www.ecofriendlyhouses.net/cardboard-house.html. p40 source: 'How Much Does One Household Produce in Recyclables?', by Karyn Maier, Demand Media, http://greenliving.nationalgeographic.com/much-one-household-produce-recyclables-2575.html; p44 source: http://www.nationalgeographic.com/adventure/photography/adventure-dreams/how-to-build-dream-house-paradise/lessons-learned.html; p52 source: 'The Canadian Oil Boom', http://ngm.nationalgeographic.com/2009/03/canadian-oil-sands/kunzig-text; p63 source: http://www.ideaconnection.com/new-inventions/smart-window-moderates-the-sun-05046.html; found on http://www.ideaconnection.com/right-brain-workouts/00236-not-so-passive-restraint.html; p77 source: http://uk.businessinsider.com/how-17-famous-companies-got-their-names-2015-7?r=US&IR=T; p86 source: http://news.nationalgeographic.com/news/2006/09/060914-oldest-writing.html; p 94 source: http://animals.nationalgeographic.com/animals/amphibians/northern-leopard-frog/?source=A-to-Z; source: http://animals.nationalgeographic.com/animals/mammals/platypus/?source=A-to-Z; source: http://animals.nationalgeographic.com/animals/reptiles/alligator-snapping-turtle/?source=A-to-Z; source: http://animals.nationalgeographic.com/animals/fish/butterflyfish/?source=A-to-Z; p103 source: www.RSPB.org.uk/wildlife birdguide/name/r/redkite/conservation.aspx; p106 source: http://www.postoffice.co.uk/letters-parcels; pp107–108 source: www.direct.gov.uk/en/Motoring/DriverLicensing/DrivingInGbOnAForeignLicence found on http://www.direct.gov.uk/en/Motoring/DriverLicensing/DrivingInGbOnAForeignLicence/DG_4022556; p109 source: http://www.adviceguide.org.uk/index/your_world/travel_index_ew/driving_tests.htm

Cover: © Awakening/Getty Images.

Photos: 4 © Rebecca Hale/National Geographic Creative; 6 © Lynn Johnson/National Geographic Creative; 7 © wavebreakmedia/Shutterstock.com; 8 © Kris Krüg; 12 © Lucy Pemoni JDP/Reuters; 15 © Doug Pensinger/Getty Images; 16 © Annelie Pompe; 17 (t) © Peter Chadwick/Getty Images; 17 (m) PhotoAlto sas/Alamy Stock Photo; 17 (b) Richard Levine/Alamy Stock Photo; 19 (tl) © OtmarW/Shutterstock.com; 19 (tr) © Rena Schild/Shutterstock.com; 19 (ml) © katacarix/Shutterstock.com; 19 (mr) © Pyshnyy Maxim Vjacheslavovich/Shutterstock.com; 19 (bl) © Denis Kuvaev/Shutterstock.com; 19 (br) © Maxisport/Shutterstock.com; 20 © MariaPavlova/iStockphoto; 21 © CHEN WS/Shutterstock.com; 22 © Beneda Miroslav/Shutterstock.com; 24 (t) © Charles W. Berry/National Geographic Creative; 24 (b) © Ed Kashi/National Geographic Creative; 28 © Brady Barr/National Geographic Creative; 29 © Sindre Lundvold/Barcroft Media/Getty Images; 30 Royal Geographical Society/Alamy Stock Photo; 32 © Elena Kalistratova/iStockphoto; 33 © Tal Karaso; 36 © wakila/iStockphoto; 37 © Mincemeat/Shutterstock.com; 39 (t) © Yvonne Witte/Wikkelhouse; 39 (m) © Sharad Raval/Shutterstock.com; 39 (b) © Eugenio Marongiu/Shutterstock.com; 40 © Joseph Sohm/Shutterstock.com; 41 © Jerome Whittingham/Shutterstock.com; 46 Thomas Cockrem/Alamy Stock Photo; 49 Art Directors & TRIP/Alamy Stock Photo; 52 © Peter Essick/National Geographic Creative; 54 (t) © Drew Aquilina and Green Pieces; 54 (b) © Drew Aquilina and Green Pieces; 56 Pep Roig/Alamy Stock Photo; 58 © flyfloor/iStockphoto; 60 © Stephen Alvarez/National Geographic Creative; 62 © Valua Vitaly/Shutterstock.com; 63 © Stacey Newman/iStockphoto; 64 © eriktham/iStockphoto; 66 Mike Goldwater/Alamy Stock Photo; 69 © Pi-Lens/Shutterstock.com; 71 Sebastian Wasek/Alamy Stock Photo 72 © photowind/Shutterstock.com; 77 © Prasong Putichanchai/Shutterstock.com; 78 (tl) © Sonkannapatchara Tapnikom/Shutterstock.com; 78 (tm) © POM POM/Shutterstock.com; 78 (tr) © Chesky/Shutterstock.com; 78 (mtl) © Viorel Sima/Shutterstock.com; 78 (mtr) © DoublePHOTO studio/Shutterstock.com; 78 (mbl) age fotostock/Alamy Stock Photo; 78 (mbr) © Leena Robinson/Shutterstock.com; 78 (bl) © bitt24/Shutterstock.com; 78 (br) © Laboko/Shutterstock.com; 80 © KorArkaR/Shutterstock.com; 82 © Jake Curtis/Getty Images; 84 (t) © NASA; 84 (mt) Directphoto Collection/Alamy Stock Photo; 84 (mmt) Pictorial Press Ltd/Alamy Stock Photo; 84 (mmb) © Media24/Gallo Images/Getty Images; 84 (mb) © Gerard Malie/AFP/Getty Images; 84 (b) © Veni/iStockphoto; 86 © AP/Press Association Images; 87 © Elena Fernandez Z/Shutterstock.com; 88 © David Ionut/Shutterstock.com; 89 imageBROKER/Alamy Stock Photo; 90 (l) Reuters/Alamy Stock Photo; 90 (r) © Popperfoto/Getty Images; 92 robertharding/Alamy Stock Photo; 94 (t) © Sista Vongjintanaruks/Shutterstock.com; 94 (mt) jack thomas/Alamy Stock Photo; 94 (mb) © Offscreen/Shutterstock.com; 94 (b) Dave Watts/Alamy Stock Photo; 95 (t) © Vladimir Chernyanskiy/Shutterstock.com; 95 (mt) © kaman985shu/Shutterstock.com; 95 (m) © Michael Wick/Shutterstock.com; 95 (mb) © Gumpanat/Shutterstock.com; 95 (b) © Mr. James Kelley/Shutterstock.com; 96 © photopopRmorse/Shutterstock.com; 98 © Neil Lang/Shutterstock.com.

Illustrations: 22, 48, 73, 138 Kevin Hopgood/Kevin Hopgood Illustration; 23 Lumina Datamatics; 31, 55, 85 Matthew Hams; 44, 52, 60 David Russell; 93 Martin Sanders.

Printed in China by RR Donnelley
Print Number: 03   Print Year: 2019

Contents

Unit 1 Lifestyle

1a Global health

Grammar present simple

1 Complete the article about Nathan Wolfe with the present simple form of the verbs.

How one scientist fights for global health

Nathan Wolfe is a scientist and he ¹ _____ (work) all over the world. He ² _____ (specialize) in viruses and diseases and he often ³ _____ (go) to places with health problems. In particular, he ⁴ _____ (study) viruses and diseases from animals. It's an important job because he ⁵ _____ (want) to know how these viruses move from animals to humans and how we can stop them in the future. As a result, Nathan ⁶ _____ (spend) a lot of time in regions with wildlife.

In the modern world, humans ⁷ _____ (not / stay) in one place anymore, and so new viruses also ⁸ _____ (travel) more easily. When humans ⁹ _____ (visit) different regions (for example, Africa), they ¹⁰ _____ (not / realize) how easy it is to bring a new kind of disease back with them.

However, the modern world with its technology also ¹¹ _____ (help) Nathan with his work. He often works in parts of the world where people ¹² _____ (not / have) electricity. But a mobile phone allows Nathan to continue his life-saving work.

Glossary
disease (n) /dɪziːz/ an illness that affects humans and animals
virus (n) /vaɪˈrəs/ a small living thing that enters a human body and makes you ill

▶ SPELL CHECK present simple (*he / she / it*) verb endings

We add *-s* to most verbs to form the present simple third person. However, note these exceptions:
- Add *-es* to verbs ending in *-ch, -o, -s, -ss, -sh* and *-x*: *watch → watches*.
- For verbs ending in *-y* after a consonant, change the *-y* to *-i* and add *-es*: *study → studies*.
- *have* and *be* have irregular forms.

2 Look at the spell check box. Then write the present simple third-person form of these verbs.

1	start _____	5	live _____
2	watch _____	6	study _____
3	fly _____	7	finish _____
4	pass _____	8	relax _____

3 Pronunciation /s/, /z/ or /ɪz/

🎧 **1** Listen to the endings of these verbs. Write the verbs in the table. Listen again and repeat.

has	helps	is	realizes	specializes	spends
stays	studies	travels	visits	wants	

/s/	/z/	/ɪz/

4 Write questions about Nathan Wolfe and his work. Use the present simple.

1 (where / Nathan / work)

.... ?

All over the world.

2 (where / he / often / go)

.... ?

To places with health problems.

3 (what / he / find and study)

.... ?

Viruses and diseases from animals.

4 (where / he / spend / a lot of time)

.... ?

In regions with wildlife.

5 (why / new viruses / travel more easily)

.... ?

Because humans travel all over the world.

6 (what / he / need / for his work)

.... ?

Modern technology.

7 (people / have electricity / every part of the world)

.... ?

No, they don't.

8 (how / Nathan / communicate)

.... ?

With a mobile phone.

Grammar adverbs of frequency

6 Put the words in order to make sentences.

1 do / always / in the evening / I / exercise

....

2 it / in the winter / always / colder / is

....

3 take / twice a day / I / this medicine

....

4 they / don't / go / often / on holiday

....

5 at weekends / we / sometimes / busy / are

....

6 eats out / rarely / she / during the week

....

7 on time / are / never / for work / you

....

8 do / check / you / your emails / always / at lunchtime / ?

....

Listening healthy living quiz

5 🖸 **2** Look at the quiz. Then listen to a conversation between two people at work. Choose the correct option (a, b or c).

Stress is bad for your health – both physical and mental

Find out how stressed you are with this quick quiz.

1 I worry about money _____ .

   a every day ⚪   b at least once a week ⚪   c once a month ⚪

2 I _____ have problems sleeping at night.

   a never ⚪   b sometimes ⚪   c always ⚪

3 I _____ find it difficult to concentrate.

   a rarely ⚪   b sometimes ⚪   c often ⚪

4 Which of these sentences describes your lunchtimes?

   a I often eat lunch at my desk and answer calls or send emails. ⚪

   b I often eat lunch at my desk and read the newspaper or relax. ⚪

   c I often leave my desk, go for a walk or eat my lunch somewhere else. ⚪

1b Mobile medicine

Reading community health

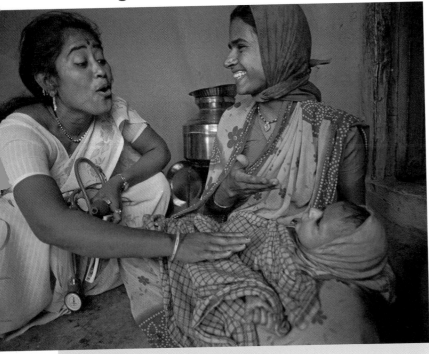

1 Read the article. Choose the correct option (a–c) to answer the questions.

1 How often does Sarubai visit people in the village?
 a once a day
 b twice a day
 c twice a week

2 How many doctors are there in the village of Jawalke?
 a one
 b two
 c none

3 Where does Rani Kale come from?
 a Jawalke
 b another village near Jawalke
 c we don't know

4 Sarubai meets Rani because she is
 a ill.
 b pregnant.
 c sick.

5 Which of these statements is true about the health workers?
 a They only deliver babies.
 b They do the same job as doctors.
 c They have many different responsibilities.

6 What is the purpose of the mobile team?
 a To do the job of the health workers.
 b To provide more medical help.
 c To train the health workers.

7 How do we know from the article that the village health project is successful?
 a Because they are training more health workers.
 b Because patients say they are happy with their health workers.
 c Because the region doesn't need any more doctors.

Mobile medicine

Sarubai Salve goes to work twice a day. She leaves her home once at nine o'clock in the morning, and then again at six o'clock in the evening, to visit people in her village of Jawalke. The village has about 240 families, and with another woman called Babai Sathe, Sarubai is responsible for the health of the village. The women visit pregnant women and give medicine to some of the older people. Today they are visiting their first patient. Rani Kale doesn't come from Jawalke. She lives about an hour away but her village doesn't have anyone like Sarubai to help mothers-to-be. Sarubai is checking Rani and she is worried about the position of the baby. Rani might need to go to hospital.

Half an hour later, Sarubai and Babai visit another mother with a three-month-old baby. While they are checking the baby, Sarubai also gives the mother advice on healthy eating and vaccinations. Jawalke is a very different place because of the two women. They regularly deliver babies and continue to help as the child grows up. There is a shortage of doctors in this region, so village health workers are important because they can give medicine and advice.

A mobile team visits Jawalke once a week. The team includes a nurse and a doctor. The mobile team meets with Sarubai and they look at any of her patients with serious medical problems. The health workers are an important connection between the mobile team and the local people. Currently there are 300 village health workers in the region and the number is growing.

Glossary
vaccination (n) /ˌvæksɪˈneɪʃ(ə)n/ medicine you put in the body to stop disease

2 Find words in the article for these definitions.

1 looks after (verb phrase) _____
2 when a woman is going to have a baby (adj)
   _____
3 a person with a medical problem who sees a doctor (n) _____
4 women who are going to have a baby (n)
   _____
5 a place for people with medical problems (n)
   _____
6 help a woman have a baby (v) _____
7 not enough of something (n) _____
8 moving from place to place (adj) _____
9 important and sometimes dangerous (adj)
   _____
10 near or in the same area (adj) _____

Grammar present continuous

3 Read the article again. Underline the present continuous forms.

4 Choose the correct option to complete the sentences.

1 At the moment *I drive / I'm driving* towards the city. Is that the right direction?
2 London *has / is having* a population of about eight million people.
3 Where *do you come / are you coming* from originally?
4 Sorry, I can't hear you because a plane *flies / is flying* overhead.
5 *I never cycle / I'm never cycling* to work in the winter.
6 Someone *stands / is standing* at the front door. Can you see who it is?
7 *Do you always leave / Are you always leaving* for work this early in the morning?
8 It was warm earlier today but now *it gets / it's getting* colder and colder.
9 We *don't stay / aren't staying* very long. It's just a short visit.
10 *Do you work / Are you working* now or *do you take / are you taking* a break?

5 Pronunciation contracted forms

🎧 **3** Listen to the sentences. Write the number of words you hear. Contracted forms (*I'm, we're, aren't, isn't* etc.) count as one word.

a ___5___   d _____
b _____   e _____
c _____   f _____

▶ **SPELL CHECK present continuous -ing endings**
- With verbs ending in -e, delete the -e then add -ing: *dance → dancing*
- With verbs ending in -ie, delete the -e and change the *i* to a *y*: *die → dying*
- With some verbs ending in one vowel and a consonant, double the final consonant: *stop → stopping, run → running*

6 Look at the spell check box. Then write the -ing form of these verbs.

1 live _____   6 lie _____
2 drop _____   7 take _____
3 let _____   8 travel _____
4 swim _____   9 get _____
5 have _____   10 jog _____

7 Dictation my typical day

🎧 **4** The man in this photo is describing his typical day. Listen and write the words you hear.

_____
_____
_____
_____
_____
_____
_____
_____
_____
_____
_____

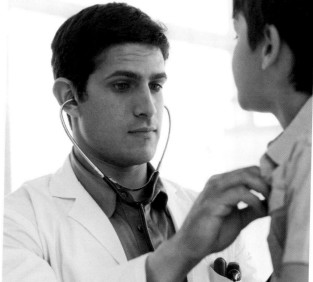

1c A happy and healthy lifestyle

Listening an interview with Elizabeth Dunn

1 🔊 **5** Listen to an interview with Elizabeth Dunn. Complete the sentences.

1   Elizabeth is interested in what makes us feel
    _____ .

2   She does research on happiness and how
    _____ affects this.

3   As part of her research she did an experiment with
    a group of _____ .

4   She thinks that experiences like visiting a new
    _____ are good for you.

2 🔊 **5** Listen again. Read these sentences and choose the correct option (a–c).

a   Elizabeth agrees.
b   Elizabeth disagrees.
c   Elizabeth doesn't say.

1   Coffee with friends is better than having lots of
    money. _____

2   Money is the most important thing. _____

3   Money doesn't make you feel happier. _____

4   Giving money to other people makes you happy.
    _____

5   Spending money on other people makes you
    happier. _____

6   Spending money on experiences makes you feel
    happy. _____

Word focus *feel*

3 Match the sentences (1–6) with the uses of *feel* (a–f).

1   I feel like going out for dinner tonight.
2   I don't feel this is the right thing to do.
3   My daughter feels ill.
4   I feel much happier today.
5   The sun feels warm. It felt much colder
    yesterday.
6   I feel like a coffee.

a   talking about your emotions
b   talking about sickness
c   giving a view or an opinion
d   talking about the weather
e   wanting something
f   wanting to do something

4 Match the questions (1–5) with the answers (a–e).

1   How are you today?
2   Do you feel like something to eat?
3   What do you think about my work in
    general?
4   Do you feel like helping me with this?
5   What's the weather like?

a   Actually, I feel you need to do more.
b   It feels freezing out there!
c   Sorry, I'm really busy at the moment.
d   Yes, a sandwich, please.
e   I'm feeling much better, thanks.

5 Write seven different questions with the word *feel*. Use these words. You can use words more than once.

a coffee	cold	doing something
like	how do you	OK	's	what

1   _____ ?
2   _____ ?
3   _____ ?
4   _____ ?
5   _____ ?
6   _____ ?
7   _____ ?

1d At the doctor's

Vocabulary medical problems

1 Complete the conversations with these words.

| back | ear | head | mouth | nose | stomach |
| throat | tooth |

1 A: Sorry, I've got a really runny _____ today.
   B: It's OK. Here's a tissue if you need one.

2 A: I've got really bad _____ ache.
   B: Is the problem in the left or the right?
   A: Both!

3 A: It's too painful to eat.
   B: It sounds like you have _____ ache. You should go to the dentist.

4 A: What's that noise?
   B: They're digging up the road outside.
   A: It's giving me a terrible _____ ache.

5 A: I can hardly talk today.
   B: Why? Have you got a sore _____ ?

6 A: Can you pick this up for me? I've got a bad _____ at the moment.
   B: Sure. But maybe you should lie down for a while.

7 A: My throat is very red, doctor.
   B: Well, let's have a look. Open your _____ , please.

8 A: What's the problem?
   B: It's my _____ . I feel a bit sick.

2 Pronunciation one or two syllables?

🔊 **6** Listen to these sentences. Find the two-syllable words and underline the stressed syllable.

1 How does your <u>sto</u>mach feel?

2 Is your throat sore or is it better?

3 Drink this hot water.

4 My headache is worse today.

5 Can I see the doctor about my ear?

6 This is good for a runny nose.

Real life talking about illness

3 🔊 **7** Listen to a conversation at the doctor's. Complete the form.

Patient's medical problems
1 Medical problem: sore throat _____ headache _____   stomach ache _____ earache _____ cough _____   other _____
2 Temperature: low _____ normal _____ high _____
3 Details of prescription: medicine _____ pills _____
4 Advice: _____   _____   _____

4 🔊 **7** Complete the conversation with these phrases. Then listen again and check.

They are good	Have you got
How do you feel	If you still feel ill
Do you feel	take this prescription
Let me have a	You need to
try drinking	Let me check

Doctor: [1] _____ today?
Patient: Not very well. I've got a terrible sore throat.
Doctor: I see. [2] _____ look. Open wide. Yes, it's very red in there.
Patient: I've also got a bad cough.
Doctor: [3] _____ sick at all?
Patient: No, not really.
Doctor: [4] _____ a temperature?
Patient: I don't think so. I don't feel hot.
Doctor: [5] _____ it … Yes, it's a bit high. Do you have anything for it?
Patient: I bought some pills at the pharmacy, but they didn't do any good.
Doctor: Well, [6] _____ to the pharmacy. [7] _____ take some different pills. [8] _____ for your throat. Take one every four hours. You need to go to bed for a couple of days, and [9] _____ lots of water.
Patient: OK. Thanks.
Doctor: [10] _____ in a few days, come back and see me, but I think it's flu. Everyone has it at the moment.

> **Glossary**
> **flu** (n) /fluː/ a common illness which makes the patient feel hot or cold with a temperature.
> **prescription** (n) /prɪˈskrɪpˈʃən/ a piece of paper from the doctor with medicine written on it. You give it to the pharmacist.

5 Listen and respond giving advice

🔊 **8** Listen to five friends with different medical problems. Respond with some advice. Then compare your advice with the model answer that follows.

> I've got a headache.

> You need to take some pills.

1e Personal information

Writing filling in a form

1 Look at the medical form. Find words and expressions in the form for these definitions (1–10).

1 What you put before your name _____ *title*
2 The first letter of your middle name _____
3 When you were born _____
4 Where to call you between 9 and 5 _____
5 How you feel overall _____
6 Times when you were very sick in the past _____
7 How much sport you do _____
8 A person to call when there is a problem _____
9 Numbers and letters at the end of your address _____
10 Your family name _____

Listening filling in a form

2 🔊 **9** Listen to a conversation at the doctor's. The receptionist is asking a new patient for information. Fill in the form with the information you hear.

3 Writing skill personal information

Complete the information from different forms with your own details.

1 Title _____
2 Surname _____
3 Occupation _____
4 Tel. no. _____
5 Middle initial(s) _____
6 Place of birth _____
7 D.O.B. _____
8 Marital status _____
9 Gender _____
10 Country of origin _____
11 No. of dependants _____
12 Name of next of kin _____

Medical Details

Title _____ First Initial _____ Middle Initial _____

Surname _____ D.O.B _____

Address _____
_____

Postcode _____ Contact no (daytime) _____

General health _____
_____

Number of hours of exercise per week _____

Type of exercise/sports _____

Last visit to doctor _____

Previous serious illnesses _____

Contact person/number (in case of emergency) _____

Wordbuilding verb + noun collocations

1 Match the verbs in A with the nouns in B to make collocations. Then complete the sentences with the collocations.

A	check	do	go	have	play
	read	run	take		

B	a book	a coffee	emails	exercise
	hiking	a marathon	the piano	
	public transport			

1 I'm training to _____ _____ next year. So far I can do about twenty kilometres.

2 I often _____ in the mountains at weekends. It's very relaxing.

3 I _____ _____ when I have time. Mozart is my favourite composer.

4 Before I sleep at night, I usually _____ _____ . Fantasy or science fiction are my favourites.

5 I _____ _____ about twice a week at the local gym.

6 I _____ _____ to work instead of driving a car.

7 I never _____ _____ my personal _____ at work. My boss doesn't want me to.

8 Can I _____ _____ with milk, please?

2 Write other verb + noun collocations for the verbs in Exercise 1.

Example:
take time, take a break, take a taxi

Learning skills recording new vocabulary

3 When you learn a new English word, how do you record it? Tick the information you record.

a the meaning
b the translation into your language
c the pronunciation (the sounds and the stress)
d the type of word (verb, adjective, noun, preposition, etc.)
e collocations
f any common phrases or expressions using this word

4 Which of these techniques do you use in your notebook?

a   Word groups

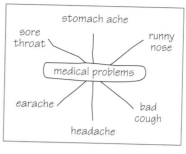

b   Drawings

go hiking

c   Diagrams

always	often	sometimes	rarely	never
100% ←		→ 50% →		→ 0%

5 Look at some of the new words from Unit 1.

1 Try recording some new information about the words. Use a dictionary to help you.

2 Try different techniques for learning the new words. Decide which techniques work well for you.

Check!

6 Complete the crossword. You can find the answers in Unit 1 of the Student's Book.

Across

3 A large Italian island
6 You do this with plants and flowers
7 When your body is too hot because you are ill
8 A person who lives to 100 years or more
10 Tired

Down

1 You can give this to a friend if they have a problem
2 Something a pharmacist or doctor gives you for an illness
4 The speed of the heart
5 A Japanese island with some of the oldest people in the world
9 A short sleep

2a Paddleboard racing

Reading adventure sport

1 Read the article. Are the sentences true (T) or false (F)?

1 Paddleboarding is a combination of two other sports.
2 Competitive paddleboard races are usually on rivers.
3 The most important race is on the ocean around Hawaii.
4 Jamie Mitchell completed the Molokai to Oahu race in the fastest time.
5 The prize money for first place in the race is three thousand dollars.
6 The writer says paddleboard racing is a famous sport.
7 Jamie is a full-time professional sportsperson.
8 Jamie loves the sport and visiting Hawaii with friends.

Paddleboard racing

Paddleboarding is a mixture of two water sports – surfing and rowing. Paddleboarding uses a surfboard and the paddleboarder 'rows' the board. However, there are two big differences. In surfing, you have to stand, but in paddleboarding you can kneel or lie on the board. In rowing you use oars, but in paddleboarding you mustn't use oars. You have to use your arms to move along.

You can do the sport on rivers, but most of the big competitions are on the ocean. The main competition for paddleboarders is the annual race from Molokai to Oahu in Hawaii. The distance is 50 kilometres. On a good day, with the right kind of waves, you don't always have to use your arms because the water carries you some of the way but, on a bad day, you are using your arms the whole way.

Competitors must be very strong and athletic. One of paddleboarding's most famous competitors is the Australian Jamie Mitchell. Not many people know about Mitchell, but he is the eight-time winner of the Molokai to Oahu race. He also has the record time of four hours, fifty-eight minutes and twenty-five seconds.

Because the sport isn't well known, the prize money for winning paddleboarding is small compared to other sports – Mitchell only received $3,000 for winning the race this year. But Mitchell obviously loves the sport because he trains two or three times a day, six days a week, for the four months before the race. At the same time, he has to earn money, so he does anything including working in bars or building work.

So how does Mitchell stay interested in such a sport? He says, 'I just love paddleboarding. It's not about winning. It's about coming to Hawaii and spending time with my good friends in a place that I love.'

2 Match these words from the article with the definitions (1–6).

> athletic   kneel   oars   rowing   surfing   waves

1   sport of riding waves on the sea
              (n)

2   sport of moving a boat through water with oars
              (n)

3   put both knees on a flat surface
              (v)

4   long pieces of wooden equipment in rowing for moving the boat   (n)

5   water on the sea that goes up and down
              (n)

6   physically strong and good at sport
              (adj)

Grammar verbs for rules

3 Rewrite these sentences using a form of *can, have to* or *must*. Sometimes, more than one verb is possible. Then compare your answers with the sentences in the article.

1   In surfing, it's obligatory to stand on your board.
In surfing, you *have to* stand on your board.

2   Paddleboarders are allowed to kneel or lie on the board.
Paddleboarders   kneel or lie on the board.

3   In paddleboarding, you are not allowed to use oars.
In paddleboarding, you   use oars.

4   It's obligatory to use your arms to move along.
You   use your arms to move along.

5   Paddleboarders are allowed to practise on rivers.
Paddleboarders   practise on rivers.

6   It's necessary for competitors to be very strong and athletic.
Competitors   be very strong and athletic.

4 Pronunciation *n't*

🔊 **10** Listen and choose the form you hear. Then listen again and repeat.

1   You *must / mustn't* play.
2   They *do / don't* have to win.
3   He *can / can't* lose the match.
4   The team *must / mustn't* score another goal.
5   A player *can / can't* hit the ball twice.

5 Write one rule for each sport (1–5). Use words from A, B and C.

> **A** Each team   The ball   The referee   You   Players

> **B** has to / must   can   don't have to
> can't / mustn't

> **C** get a red card.
> go over the net.
> stop the match.
> have five people on the court.
> use any special equipment.

1   Basketball: *Each team has to / must have five players on the court.*

2   Football:

3   Rugby:

4   Running:

5   Tennis:

Vocabulary competitions

6 Complete the sentences with one word. The first letter is given.

1   My local team got to the final of the c   , but they lost in the end.

2   W   at the Olympics get a gold medal because they beat all the other competitors.

3   The final s   in the tennis match was three sets to one.

4   Two runners crossed the finish l   at the same time so they both came first.

5   The r   gave two red cards and six yellow cards during the match.

6   'Which is your favourite t   ?' 'The one in red.'

7   Can you explain the r   of American football? I don't understand them.

8   There were 48,000 s   at the football match.

2b Sports and leisure activities

Reading walking football

1 Read the article and answer the questions with words from the article.

1 Do more people watch the World Cup or the Olympic Games on TV?

2 Which type of teams play football every weekend?

3 How old are the players in walking football?

4 Why is it good for older people?

5 Which two rules are different from normal football?

6 Why don't many people watch walking football?

7 How many teams play walking football in the United Kingdom?

Walking football

Globally, more people play football than any other sport, and more people watch the World Cup on TV than the Olympic Games. Every weekend, thousands of teams meet in different countries to compete against each other. That includes famous teams such as Real Madrid and Manchester United, and local teams of people playing competitively and for fun. From an early age, school children play football in their physical education lessons and compete against teams from other schools. Now, there is a new type of football which is growing in popularity. It's called 'walking football'.

Most footballers retire from competitive games in their thirties, but walking football is for the over fifties. It's a great way to keep fit and it can help older people live longer. Doctors also say it's good for the mind and relaxation. Most walking football matches are informal and social. Most of the rules are the same as for normal football, but everything is much slower. Players have to walk with the ball – they can't run. Also, players have to keep one foot on the ground all the time so they can't jump.

Not surprisingly, walking football doesn't get many spectators because it is very slow. But more and more people like playing it; for example, in the United Kingdom there were around 100 teams two years ago. Now there are over 800, with regular competitions in different parts of the country every year.

2 Vocabulary extra talking about likes and dislikes

a Match the highlighted verbs in the speech bubbles with the emoticons (a–f).

> I enjoy swimming when I have time.

> I love winning!

> I really like watching sport on TV.

> I hate boxing.

> I can't stand losing!

> I don't mind playing cricket but I don't like watching it.

a ☺ ☺ ☺ ....

b ☺ ☺ ....

c ☺   like, ...

d ☹ ....

e ☹   dislike, ...

f ☹ ☹ .... , ...

b Complete the sentences so they are true for you.

1 I love playing ....

2 I enjoy .... when I have time.

3 I don't mind ....

4 I don't like watching .... on TV.

5 I can't stand ....

Grammar *-ing* form

3 Complete the sentences with the *-ing* form of these verbs.

be	become	compete	cycle	fly
learn	lose	~~play~~	sit	watch

1 *Playing* tennis is fun and it's very good for your health.

2 _____ in a match is only fun if you win.

3 We love _____ because you get fit and see the countryside.

4 _____ to play the piano takes years of practice.

5 When I play games, I'm not good at _____. I get really angry.

6 _____ in front of the TV all day isn't good for you.

7 Are you interested in _____ in our team?

8 I don't like travelling by plane because I'm afraid of _____.

9 Have you ever thought of _____ a professional sportsperson in the future?

10 You play golf every week so why do you hate _____ it on TV?

4 Pronunciation /ŋ/

a 🎧 **11** Listen to these words and underline the part of the word with the /ŋ/ sound.

1 watching
2 language
3 waiting
4 thinks
5 cycling
6 losing
7 winning
8 English
9 competing
10 thanks

b Listen again and repeat the words.

5 Dictation Kristi Leskinen

🎧 **12** Listen to part of a documentary about the skier Kristi Leskinen. Complete the text with the words you hear.

Kristi Leskinen is a famous skier. She ¹ _____

but her favourite place is Mammoth Mountain in the USA. ² _____

such as kayaking, but she ³ _____.

Recently she was in a TV show called *The Superstars*. In the show, famous ⁴ _____

that ⁵ _____.

Kristi won ⁶ _____.

But soon it's winter again so she needs to go back to the mountains and start training again. This year ⁷ _____

a lot more medals.

2c Dangerous sports

Listening freediving

1 🎵 **13** Listen to a sports programme about Annelie Pompe, a freediver. Number the topics (a–d) in the order the presenter talks about them.

a when Annelie climbed Mount Everest
b a definition of freediving
c why Annelie Pompe likes freediving
d why she likes doing other sports

2 🎵 **13** Listen again. Choose the correct option (a–c) to complete the sentences.

1 Freediving is an underwater sport. The diver
   _____ .
   a has to use breathing equipment
   b doesn't have to use breathing equipment
   c can't use breathing equipment

2 Annelie's world record is a dive of _____ metres.
   a 120   b 126   c 136

3 She spends every _____ training in the sea.
   a day   b week   c weekend

4 She _____ other sports.
   a likes doing
   b doesn't have time for
   c doesn't like doing

5 For Annelie, adventure is about going to the _____ parts of the world!
   a highest
   b deepest
   c highest and deepest

Word focus *like*

3 Match the sentences (1–7) with the different uses of *like* (a–g).

1 He's like his older brother. He was good at athletics too.
2 He looks like his older brother. He has black hair, too.
3 I'd like to win a gold medal one day.
4 I'd like a cup of coffee, please.
5 Do you feel like going out later?
6 I like most sports.
7 I like watching most sports.

a to say you feel people or things are good (*like* + noun)
b to say you enjoy doing something (*like* + -*ing*)
c use with *would* to say you want to do something in the future (*would like* + *to* + infinitive)
d use with *would* to say you want something (*would like* + noun)
e to describe similar behaviour to something or someone
f used with the verbs *look*, *smell*, *sound* and *taste* to describe similarities with someone or something (*look like*, etc.)
g use with *feel* to talk about wanting to do something (*feel like* + -*ing*)

4 Rewrite the sentences using the word *like*.

1 They want to play tennis later.
   They *'d like to play tennis later* . OR
   They *feel like playing tennis later* .

2 You're very similar in appearance to someone I went to school with.
   You _____ I went to school with.

3 She wants to play tennis professionally one day.
   She _____ tennis professionally one day.

4 We want some ice cream, please.
   We _____ , please.

5 He isn't similar to his sister. She always worked very hard.
   He _____ his sister. She always worked very hard.

2d Joining a group

Reading leaflet for a fitness class

1 Read the leaflet for fitness classes at a local gym. Match the sentences (1–7) with the classes (A–C).

1. You have to get up early for this class.
2. The person in charge tells you what to do.
3. This class is good after a day at work.
4. This class mixes enjoyment with exercise.
5. Take a break from work and come for some exercise.
6. You will notice a difference very quickly.
7. It lasts for an hour and a half.

Fit for Life Gym

A

◀ Boot camp starts at 6 a.m. every morning with your instructor. He shouts orders and you run, jump, lift. It's non-stop exercise for 90 minutes.

'Perfect for people who want fast results.'

Our evening Pilates ▶ **B** classes help your body to recover after a hard day at work. Build strength with an exercise programme suitable for any age and fitness level.

'After a day in the office chair, Pilates is perfect for your muscles.'

C

◀ Our Zumba classes are a mixture of fun, excitement and high energy levels. Classes are at midday, so you can even join us during your lunch break.

'Zumba is a fun way to get fit – every class feels like a party!'

Real life talking about interests

2 🎵 **14** Listen to two friends talking about the leaflet. Number the fitness classes in the order they discuss them.

Boot Camp   Pilates   Zumba

3 🎵 **14** Listen again. Complete the conversation.

A: Hey, this looks interesting.
B: What?
A: This leaflet for fitness classes at the gym. Are you ¹ _____ _____ doing something like that?
B: Maybe. But I'm ² _____ _____ good at sport.
A: But this isn't competitive. It's for getting fit. This one ³ _____ _____ . Boot Camp. What about joining that?
B: What is Boot Camp?
A: It's like the army. You have someone who tells you what to do. I think ⁴ _____ _____ do it.
B: When is it?
A: At six.
B: Great. So we can go after work.
A: No, it's six in the morning.
B: What?! You must be joking. I hate getting up early. ⁵ _____ _____ doing something later?
A: Well, there's one at lunchtime. It's called Zumba. It's a kind of dance, I think.
B: I don't like dancing.
A: ⁶ _____ _____ . It looks fun.
B: What about something after work?
A: There's a Pilates class. It doesn't say an exact time, but it says it's after work.
B: Well, ⁷ _____ _____ that to Boot Camp or dancing.
A: Yes, ⁸ _____ _____ good.

4 Listen and respond **saying what you are interested in doing**

🎵 **15** A friend wants you to join one of the classes on the leaflet in Exercise 1. You are only interested in doing Pilates. Listen to your friend and respond each time. Then compare your responses with the answers that follow.

Are you interested in Boot Camp?

No, I wouldn't like to do it.

2e Advertising an event

Writing an advert or notice

1 Imagine you are organizing a social event for everyone after work. Write a notice for everyone and tell them:

- it's a barbecue in the local park with a 'fun' football match afterwards.
- the date and time.
- the reason (it's a way for everyone to meet each other).
- your email address (so they can say if they are coming)

2 Grammar extra punctuation rules

Complete the list of rules for punctuation with these words.

> apostrophe   capital letter
> comma   exclamation mark
> full stop

1   You have to use a _____ when it's the first word of a sentence; with names of people, places and countries; with days of the week and months; and with people's titles.

2   You must end a sentence with a _____ or you can emphasize something with an _____ .

3   A _____ can separate lists of nouns or adjectives and sometimes two clauses in a sentence.

4   You have to use an _____ with contracted forms and with the possessive 's.

3 Writing skill checking and correcting your writing

Read the piece of writing by a student. Three lines are correct and seven lines have punctuation mistakes. Tick (✓) the correct lines and correct the other lines.

> My free time
>
> i have many different hobbies
> and interests such as computer
> gaming cycling and painting but
> my favourite is ice hockey. Its a
> very popular sport in my home
> country of canada. I practise
> every saturday morning at our
> local sports centre with my team
> and we play matches once a month
> We love to win

1   *I (capital letter)*
2   ✓
3   _____
4   _____
5   _____
6   _____
7   _____
8   _____
9   _____
10 _____

Wordbuilding suffixes

1 Complete the word for the sports person shown in the picture.

1 golf............

2 cycl............

3 swim............

4 rac............
driv............

5 athle............

6 run............

Learning skills using a dictionary (1)

2 Match the different parts of the dictionary entries (1–12) with these words.

adjective	definition
example sentence	first meaning
main stress	noun
past participle	plural form
present participle	pronunciation
second meaning	verb

Check!

3 Complete the sentences with these numbers. You can find the answers in Unit 2 of the Student's Book.

1.50	2	4	5	42	60	180	300

1 In the Ironman competition, you have to cycle .... kilometres.
2 Over .... competitors enter the Beard and Moustache competition in Alaska every year.
3 A Mud Bowl match lasts .... minutes.
4 Esperanza pays $ .... to watch the wrestling.
5 There are .... syllables in *competition*.
6 At the annual Idiotarod race, there are .... people in a team.
7 The match was a draw. The score was two – ....
8 Competitors in a marathon must run .... kilometres.

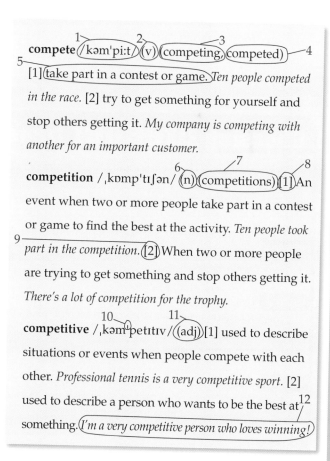

compete /kəm'pi:t/ (v) (competing, competed)
[1] take part in a contest or game. *Ten people competed in the race.* [2] try to get something for yourself and stop others getting it. *My company is competing with another for an important customer.*

competition /ˌkɒmp'tɪʃən/ (n) (competitions) [1] An event when two or more people take part in a contest or game to find the best at the activity. *Ten people took part in the competition.* [2] When two or more people are trying to get something and stop others getting it. *There's a lot of competition for the trophy.*

competitive /ˌkəm'petɪtɪv/ (adj) [1] used to describe situations or events when people compete with each other. *Professional tennis is a very competitive sport.* [2] used to describe a person who wants to be the best at something. *I'm a very competitive person who loves winning!*

3a Choosing greener transport

Reading green transport

1 Read the article. What is the aim of the article? Choose the correct option (a–c).
 a to give an opinion about transport
 b to argue for more public transport
 c to give information about a new type of transport

2 Read the article again. Are the sentences true (T) or false (F), according to the information in the article?

 1 The author thinks walking is better than driving when you visit a city.
 2 Renting bicycles from hotels and hostels can be very expensive.
 3 The author thinks cities need to give more information to visitors.
 4 Buses, trains and ferries are better for the environment than cars or aeroplanes.
 5 All hotels have charging stations for electric cars.

Vocabulary transport nouns

3 Match words from A with words from B to make compound nouns for transport. Then complete the sentences with the compound nouns.

A fuel	public	rush	speed	traffic

B hour	jam	limit	transport	costs

 1 The _____ begins at around eight and ends at around nine in my city.
 2 There's a huge _____ all the way from the city centre to the airport. Nothing is moving.
 3 It's really expensive to have a car. _____ _____ go up every year!
 4 My city has excellent _____ _____. The buses are regular and the trains are on time.
 5 Police are using cameras to catch anyone driving over the _____.

Choosing greener transport

For tourists and travellers who want a more interesting experience when they arrive in a new city or country, here are some better ways to travel, both for you and for the environment.

Step 1 Get out of the car and walk. It's slower but it's the greenest way to travel. It's also the most rewarding way to see a city, but remember to pack comfortable shoes.

Step 2 Cycling is also a good alternative. Many hotels and hostels now offer free bicycles for guests. Some also provide electric bikes that give you help with hills and on longer journeys. Some cities have bike stations. You pick up a bicycle from one of these stations and return it after two hours. It costs something but it's much cheaper than a bus or taxi.

Step 3 If you have to take transport in a city, try to take public transport. Most cities now offer lots of information and very clear maps. You'll also get more detailed information by visiting the city website before you go, so it'll save a lot of time once you get there.

Step 4 Whenever possible, take buses, trains or ferries for travelling from city to city. They are usually greener than cars and aeroplanes.

Step 5 And when the only way to travel is by car, rent a hybrid or electric car. Many car rental companies now offer this kind of choice so always ask. Look for hotels at your destination with free electric vehicle charging stations. You'll be surprised at how many hotels now offer this facility.

by Jeannette Belliveau, Demand Media

Grammar comparatives and superlatives

4 Look at the article again and underline the examples of comparative and superlative forms.

> **▶ SPELL CHECK comparatives and superlatives**
> - Add *-er* or *-est* to short adjectives: *young – younger – youngest*
> - When the adjectives end in *-e*, add *-r* or *-st*: *large – larger – largest*
> - Change adjectives ending in *-y* (after a consonant) to *-i* and add *-er* or *-est*: *happy – happier – happiest*
> - Double the final consonant of adjectives ending with a consonant + vowel + consonant: *hot – hotter – hottest*
> - Don't double the consonant for adjectives ending in vowel + *-w* or *-y*: *slow – slower – slowest*

5 Look at the spell check box. Then write the comparative and superlative forms of the adjectives.

1	cheap	*cheaper* — *cheapest*
2	angry	
3	large	
4	big	
5	safe	
6	funny	
7	thin	
8	low	
9	easy	
10	green	
11	fit	
12	fast	

6 Write sentences that give your opinion. Use a comparative form with *-er*, *more* or *less*.

1 travelling by bus / travelling by car (relaxing)

I think *travelling by bus is more relaxing than travelling by car.*

2 cake / bread (tasty)

I think

3 email / letters (fast)

I think

4 teachers / politicians (work hard)

I think

5 trains / aeroplanes (bad for the environment)

I think

7 Complete the text about transport world records with the superlative forms of these adjectives.

dangerous	fast	large	long	small	tall

WORLD RECORDS TRANSPORT

- Gregory Dunham built the world's
  1 _____ rideable motorbike. It's 3.429 metres high.
- The 2 _____ jet aircraft in the world is only 3.7 metres long and 5.7 metres wide (including wings).
- Marek Turowski drove the world's
  3 _____ motorized sofa! The piece of furniture travelled at a speed of 148 kilometres per hour.
- Emil and Liliana Schmid took the
  4 _____ journey ever. They drove 641,115 kilometres – and they are still driving!
- Billy Baxter broke the record for the fastest speed on a motorbike without seeing. He wore a blindfold over his eyes and reached 265.33 kilometres per hour. So it was probably one of the 5 _____ journeys ever as well.
- In 2008, 490 Ferraris drove round a track in Japan. That's the 6 _____ number of Ferraris in one place ever.

8 Pronunciation sentence stress in comparative and superlative sentences

🔊 **16** Listen to these sentences and underline the stressed words. Then listen again and repeat.

1 Your car is faster than mine.
2 Bicycles are the greenest transport.
3 Walking is slower than cycling.
4 Trains are cheaper than planes.
5 Hybrid transport is the most efficient.

3b World transport

Reading beautiful animals

1 Read the article about camels and answer the questions.

1 Why are camels famous?

2 What are the different ways humans use them?

3 Does everyone agree that camels aren't beautiful?

4 How long does the competition last?

5 How many camels enter the competition?

6 What do the family and friends eat at the party?

Grammar *as ... as*

2 Put the words in order. Start with the words in bold.

1 modern transport / in the forest / good as / **Horses** / are as

2 is always / as this in / my country / **The weather** / as hot

3 expensive / **Silver** / isn't / as / as gold

4 as cars / from / aren't / the sixties / **New cars** / stylish / as

5 **Bicycles** / as / cars / are / in the city centre / as fast

6 as I / used / not as / to be / **I'm** / young

3 Pronunciation /əz/

🔊 **17** /əz/ is the sound of *as* in sentences with *as ... as*. Listen to the sentences in Exercise 2 and repeat them using this sound.

Beauty competitions for camels

Camels are famous for their ability to travel through the hot desert with heavy loads. But people don't only use them for transport. Camels also produce milk to drink and meat to eat. So everyone agrees that they are useful animals, but how many of us would describe camels as beautiful? Camels have a large hump, strange knees, skinny legs and ugly teeth. They are NOT beautiful. But not everyone agrees.

Once a year, people bring their camels from the countries of Oman, Saudi Arabia, Qatar and even further away, to an area of land in Abu Dhabi. They are here to find the most beautiful camel. The competition lasts ten days. There are around 24,000 camels in the competition and the judges have to find two for the final day. The winning camel must have good ears, a high back, shiny hair and a long neck, and long legs are also important. There is a prize for the winner but this isn't as important as family honour.

This year, the winner is a man called Bin Tanaf. Immediately, his family and friends celebrate, and the party at his tent lasts all night. Two hundred people are there. They sing songs and tell stories about camels. Bin Tanaf's father says, 'This is the best day of my life.' In the middle of the celebration there is a lot of food, including rice and meat. Another man brings a large plate into the tent. There is a large piece of yellow meat on it. 'Ah,' says the son. 'The hump.'

Glossary
hump (n) / hʌmp /
honour (n) / ˈɒnə / respect for someone who does something important

Word focus *as*

4 You can use *as* in different ways. Match the sentences (1–4) with the uses of *as* (a–d).

1 As we're late, we'll take a taxi instead of the bus.
2 That car looks as if it's very old.
3 Travelling to Edinburgh by train is as fast as travelling by plane.
4 As we drove past a field, we saw a horse pulling some logs.

a to compare two things
b to talk about appearance
c to talk about two actions happening at the same time
d to talk about the reason for something

5 Rewrite the sentences using *as*.

1 We stopped for lunch because there was a traffic jam on the motorway.
   We stopped for lunch _____ _____ on the motorway.
2 You look like you had a long journey.
   _____ if you had a long journey.
3 In the city, the speed of a bicycle is the same as a bus.
   In the city, _____ fast as a bus.
4 We saw an elephant when we drove home!
   We saw an elephant _____ _____ !

Vocabulary transport adjectives

6 Read the conversation between two friends visiting London. Replace the words in bold with these words.

| convenient | comfortable | frequent |
| traditional | punctual | reliable |

A: Let's get a bus to Oxford Street. My guide book says they are ¹**regular** and ²**always on time**. There's one coming now.
B: But it doesn't say 'Oxford Street' on the front. Can we get a black cab? They are very ³**old**.
A: But it'll be expensive!
B: I know. But it's ⁴**easy**. Buses are never ⁵**there when you need them**. Look! This taxi's stopping.
A: Wow! This is so ⁶**nice to sit in**! Much better than the bus.

1 _____   4 _____
2 _____   5 _____
3 _____   6 _____

Grammar comparative modifiers

7 Read the information about transport in five countries. Then underline the correct modifying adjectives in the sentences (1–8).

	CARS	MOTORBIKES	BICYCLES
France	83%	12%	59%
South Korea	84%	9%	63%
Brazil	47%	29%	53%
South Africa	31%	7%	16%

1 The percentage of people with a car is *a bit / a lot* lower in France than in South Korea.
2 Cars are *much / a little* more popular than motorbikes in France.
3 The percentage of people with bicycles in South Korea is *a little / much* higher than in France.
4 In South Korea, bicycles are *a bit / a lot* more popular than motorbikes.
5 In Brazil, the percentage of people with cars is *a little / much* lower than the percentage of people with bicycles.
6 Motorbikes are *a lot / a bit* less popular than cars in Brazil.
7 The percentage of people with bicycles in South Africa is *much / a little* lower than in Brazil.
8 In South Africa motorbikes are *much / a bit* less popular than in South Korea.

	CARS	MOTORBIKES	BICYCLES
Italy	89%	26%	63%
Indonesia	4%	8%	65%
Malaysia	82%	83%	53%

8 Look at the results for three more countries and complete sentences 1–4. Use a modifier and the comparative form of the adjective in brackets.

1 The percentage of people with a car is _____ in Italy than in Indonesia. (high)
2 Bicycles are _____ than motorbikes in Italy. (popular)
3 The percentage of people with bicycles in Malaysia is _____ than in Indonesia. (low)
4 In Malaysia, cars are _____ than motorbikes. (popular)

3c Transport in India

Listening the Golden Quadrilateral

1 🔊 **18** Listen to a documentary about a new road in India called 'the Golden Quadrilateral'. Number the topics (a–d) in the order the presenter talks about them.
  a transport and industry on the road
  b a new road will help the economy
  c the length and technology of the new road
  d Indians are buying more and more cars

> **Glossary**
> **poverty** (n) /ˈpɒvəti/ a situation where people are poor and do not have money to pay for basic things
> **highway** (American English) (n) /ˈhaɪweɪ/ **motorway** (British English) (n) /ˈməʊtəweɪ/ a large road with many lanes
> **symbol** (n) /ˈsɪmb(ə)l/ something or someone that represents an idea

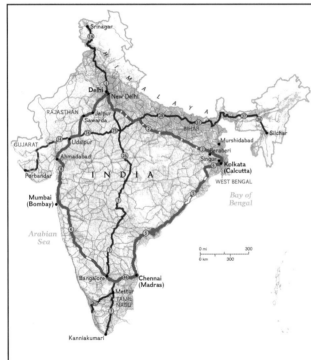

2 🔊 **18** Listen again and answer the questions. Choose the correct answer (a–c).

  1 How many new cars every year will people probably buy in the next few years?
    a 1.5 million
    b two million
    c three million

  2 Where do many of the rich people live?
    a next to the new road
    b in the cities
    c in the countryside

  3 How long is the road?
    a 600 kilometres
    b 6,000 kilometres
    c 60,000 kilometres

  4 What types of transport can you see on the road?
    a all types
    b mostly cars
    c the presenter doesn't say

  5 Why does the presenter describe the new road as 'a symbol of India's future'?
    a Because it's the same shape as the country of India.
    b Because it is modern, it is helping the economy to grow.
    c Because India has lots of transport.

Vocabulary transport verbs

3 Cross out the verb which is not possible in each group of collocations (1–6).

  1 *catch / miss / go by / ~~pick up~~* a train
  2 *drop off / take / catch / pick up* a passenger
  3 *catch / go by / get on / take* a flight
  4 *miss / go in / get / take* a taxi
  5 *ride / go by / get off / go in* (a) bicycle
  6 *get / take / miss / go* a bus

4 Pronunciation /æ/ or /eɪ/

🔊 **19** Match these words with the vowel sounds. Then listen, check and repeat.

catch	change	day	gate	jam	plan
plane	rank	take	taxi	train	

/æ/ ....
/eɪ/ ....

3d Getting around town

Vocabulary taking transport

1 Complete the sentences with these words.

book	check in	fare	gate	platform
rank	receipt	stop		

1 What's the bus _____ to the airport?
2 There's a taxi _____ by the station, so you can get one there.
3 Is there a bus _____ near here?
4 Would you like a _____ for your shopping?
5 Flight BA 387 leaves from _____ 29 in fifteen minutes.
6 The train to Dublin is arriving at _____ 3.
7 Where do I need to _____ for my flight?
8 It's often cheaper to _____ your ticket online.

Real life going on a journey

2 🔊 **20** Listen to four conversations. Match the conversations (1–4) with the type of transport (a–d).

a taxi   b bus   c train   d plane

3 🔊 **20** Listen again and answer the questions.

Conversation 1
1 Where does the bus stop?
_____

2 What kind of ticket does he buy?
_____

Conversation 2
3 How much is a first-class ticket?
_____

4 What time does it leave?
_____

5 Which platform does it leave from?
_____

Conversation 3
6 How many bags is the person checking in?
_____

7 How much extra does she pay?
_____

8 Can she pay by credit card?
_____

Conversation 4
9 Why can't the taxi stop where the person wants?
_____

10 How much is the taxi fare?
_____

4 Complete the four conversations with these phrases.

Can I have	Can I pay	Do you go
Have you got	How many	How much
I'd like a	Which platform	

Conversation 1
A: Hi. [1] _____ to the centre?
B: Which part?
A: Near the cinema.
B: Yes, we stop outside it.
A: Great. [2] _____ a return ticket, please?

Conversation 2
A: [3] _____ first-class ticket, please.
B: That's twenty euros fifty.
A: Here you are. [4] _____ is it?
B: It's at five fifteen from platform twelve.

Conversation 3
A: [5] _____ bags are you checking in?
B: Two. And I've got a carry-on.
A: I'm afraid your ticket only includes one bag. You'll have to pay an extra ten pounds for that one.
B: Oh, OK. [6] _____ by credit card?
A: Sure.

Conversation 4
A: It's just up here on the right. You can drop me off over there.
B: I can't stop there. It's a bus stop. But here's OK.
A: OK. [7] _____ is that?
B: That's thirteen dollars thirty cents.
[8] _____ the right change?

5 Listen and respond **responding to questions about travel**

🔊 **21** Listen to five questions about travel. Respond to the question with a phrase from the box. Then compare your response with the model answer that follows.

Return, please.	No, with cash.	Platform nine.
Yes, this one.	Yes, I do. Here you are.	

What kind of train ticket would you like?

Return, please.

3e Quick communication

1 Dictation telephone messages

🎵 **22** Listen to three mobile phone messages. Write every word you hear in each message.

Message one

> **WHILE YOU WERE OUT**
> _____ called at _____ a.m. / p.m.
> MESSAGE:
> _____
> _____
> _____
> _____
> _____
> _____
> _____

Message two

> **WHILE YOU WERE OUT**
> _____ called at _____ a.m. / p.m.
> MESSAGE:
> _____
> _____
> _____
> _____
> _____
> _____
> _____

Message three

> **WHILE YOU WERE OUT**
> _____ called at _____ a.m. / p.m.
> MESSAGE:
> _____
> _____
> _____
> _____
> _____
> _____

Writing notes and messages

2 Look at the messages you wrote in Exercise 1. Rewrite them in note form. Remember to miss out words like articles, pronouns, auxiliary verbs and polite forms.

Message one

> **WHILE YOU WERE OUT**
> _____ called at _____ a.m. / p.m.
> MESSAGE:
> _____
> _____
> _____

Message two

> **WHILE YOU WERE OUT**
> _____ called at _____ a.m. / p.m.
> MESSAGE:
> _____
> _____
> _____

Message three

> **WHILE YOU WERE OUT**
> _____ called at _____ a.m. / p.m.
> MESSAGE:
> _____
> _____
> _____

Wordbuilding compound nouns

> ▶ **WORDBUILDING compound nouns**
>
> Compound nouns are nouns with either:
> - two nouns joined together, e.g. *motor + bike = motorbike*.
> - two nouns together but as separate words, e.g. *car + parking = car parking*.
>
> There is no rule for when you join the words or keep them as separate words, so check in your dictionary.

1 Look at the wordbuilding box. Then complete the compound nouns in the sentences with these words.

> centre   credit   driver   seat   snow
> time   town   transport

1 Sorry, we don't accept .... cards, only cash.
2 He works at night so he often sleeps in the day ....
3 There are roadworks in the town .... so you shouldn't drive to the cinema this evening.
4 I know I should take public .... but it's easier to drive my own car.
5 A .... mobile looks like a lot of fun to drive.
6 Do you have any change to pay the taxi .... ?
7 The .... council is meeting tonight to discuss the problem of car parking.
8 I always book a window .... when I travel by plane.

2 Match words from A with words from B to make compound nouns.

> A ~~alarm~~ bank boxing football letter
> mobile tennis town

> B account box centre ~~clock~~ court gloves
> phone pitch

1 .... *alarm clock*
2 ....
3 ....
4 ....
5 ....
6 ....
7 ....
8 ....

Learning skills remembering new vocabulary

3 Look at the list of ways to remember new vocabulary. Tick (✓) the ones you use now and put an asterix (*) by the ones you would like to use in the future.

Ways to remember new vocabulary

1 After I finish a unit in the Student's Book, I read it again a few weeks later and check any words I don't remember. ◯

2 When I find a new word or expression in the unit, I highlight it. ◯

3 I write a new word on a piece of paper. On the other side of the paper, I write a definition. Then I test myself a few weeks later. ◯

4 When I find a new word, I check in my dictionary for other word forms that I can use, e.g. *commute (v), commuter (n)*. ◯

5 I write new words in lists with the translations next to them. Then I cover the words and try to translate them from my own language. ◯

6 I write the new word in a sentence that is important to me. ◯

7 I read more texts on similar subjects to the unit. I usually find some of the new words in the text. ◯

8 I choose ten new words and write a short story using them all. ◯

4 Do you use other techniques for learning and remembering vocabulary? Write them down and compare your ideas with other students in your next lesson.

Check!

5 Put the letters in the correct order to make words from Unit 3 in the Student's Book. (The clues in brackets will help.)

1 GLEDES (a type of transport) ....
2 LAKATOK (a city in India) ....
3 RODIDTIA (a famous dog race) ....
4 NARK (where taxis stop and wait) ....
5 GEGLUAG (another word for bags you take on holiday) ....
6 JETACDIVE (type of word between *as* and *as*) ....

4a Challenges and adventures

1 Vocabulary extra adventure

Replace the words in bold with these similar words or phrases.

adventure   ambition   a big challenge
my biggest achievement   crazy
dangerous   take risks

1 I don't like to **do things that could be dangerous**. ....
2 My life is so boring. I want a life of **doing exciting things**. ....
3 Don't walk so close to the cliff. It looks **unsafe**. ....
4 Passing my exams at university was **the thing that needed the most hard work and effort** in my life so far. ....
5 Climbing Mount Everest presents mountaineers with **something that is really difficult to do**, but that's what makes it worth doing! ....
6 As I get older, I have less and less **I want to achieve**. ....
7 It's snowing outside. We can't walk a hundred kilometres in this weather! Are you completely **mad**? ....

Grammar past simple

2 Look at the spell check box. Then write the past simple form of these regular verbs.

> ▶ SPELL CHECK past simple regular verbs
> (-ed endings)
>
> • Add -ed to verbs ending in a consonant: watch →
>   watched
> • Add -d to verbs ending in -e: dance → danced
> • With verbs ending in –y (after a consonant), change
>   the y to i and add -ed: cry → cried
> • Don't change the y to i after a vowel: play → played
> • Double the final consonant for most verbs ending
>   with consonant + vowel + consonant: stop → stopped

1 visit ....
2 arrive ....
3 dry ....
4 stay ....
5 jog ....
6 live ....
7 study ....
8 move ....

3 Complete the article below and on page 29 with the past simple form of these verbs.

The TV presenter

~~be born~~   become   go   start   study   survive

The circus performer

grow up   join   learn   play

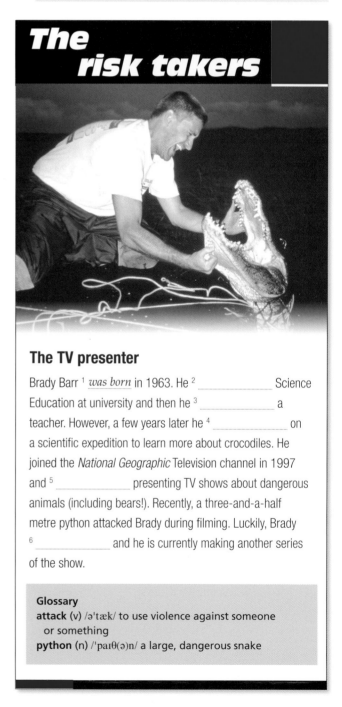

The risk takers

The TV presenter

Brady Barr [1] *was born* in 1963. He [2] .... Science
Education at university and then he [3] .... a
teacher. However, a few years later he [4] .... on
a scientific expedition to learn more about crocodiles. He
joined the *National Geographic* Television channel in 1997
and [5] .... presenting TV shows about dangerous
animals (including bears!). Recently, a three-and-a-half
metre python attacked Brady during filming. Luckily, Brady
[6] .... and he is currently making another series
of the show.

> **Glossary**
> **attack** (v) /ə'tæk/ to use violence against someone
>   or something
> **python** (n) /'paɪθ(ə)n/ a large, dangerous snake

The circus performer

Eskil Ronningsbakken [7] _____ in Norway. As a child, he enjoyed climbing trees and he [8] _____ on the roofs of houses. He [9] _____ to do a handstand when he was five and he studied circus skills when he was eight. Aged seventeen, he [10] _____ a circus, but two years later he started performing on his own with his balancing act.

4 Read the article again. Are these sentences true (T) or false (F)? Rewrite the false sentences to make them correct.

1 Brady was born in Norway.
   F – Eskil was born in Norway.

2 Both men studied at university.

3 Eskil was interested in the circus when he was a child.

4 Eskil joined a theatre when he was seventeen.

5 Brady joined a TV channel in 1997.

6 Brady attacked a python on his TV show.

7 Eskil started performing with a group of people after he left the circus.

8 Both men took risks in their life.

5 The journalist asked Brady and Eskil these questions. Complete the questions with the past simple form.

1 ' _____ born?'
   'In 1963.'

2 'Where _____ ?'
   'In Norway.'

3 'What subject _____ ?'
   'Science Education.'

4 'When _____ to do a handstand?'
   'When I was five.'

5 ' _____ *National Geographic* TV?'
   'In 1997.'

6 ' _____ performing on your own?'
   'When I was nineteen.'

6 Pronunciation past simple irregular verbs

a Write the past simple form of these verbs. (Check your answers in a dictionary.)

1 bite   _____
2 buy   _____
3 hit   _____
4 do   _____
5 say   _____
6 go   _____
7 fight _____
8 bring _____
9 meet   _____

b 🔘 **23** Listen and check. Write the verb forms you hear in the correct column of the table.

/e/	/ɪ/	/ɔː/

4b Survival stories

Vocabulary personal qualities

1 Read the clues and complete the crossword with words describing personal qualities.

Across

2 happy to wait for other people if necessary

5 a good employee who works long hours when it's necessary

6 good at learning and understanding

7 with lots of knowledge about his or her area of work

Down

1 always gets on with other people

3 happy, optimistic and likes a challenge

4 thinks about other people and how they feel

2 Pronunciation word stress

a 🔊 **24** Listen and check. Underline the syllable that is stressed.

Example:
positive

b 🔊 **24** Listen again and repeat.

Reading books and films of true stories

3 Read the article. Then match the stories (A–E) with the statements (1–8) on page 31. Sometimes more than one story matches a statement.

Survival stories

Some of the best films and books come from true stories. This is particularly true for stories about mountaineers and explorers. Here are five of the best stories which became books and films.

A In 1996 Jon Krakauer went to Mount Everest. He wanted to climb the mountain and write about how the mountain was changing. However, while he was there, eight people died in terrible weather on the side of the mountain. Krakauer described what happened in his book *Into Thin Air*.

B When a plane was flying over the Andes in 1972, it crashed but some of the passengers survived. Two Uruguayan men, Nando Parrado and Roberto Canessa, walked for many days across the mountains to get help. Their story became a film called *Alive*.

C In 1865, while Edward Whymper and his team were climbing the Matterhorn mountain, one of the men fell. As he fell, his rope pulled others down with him. Whymper survived and wrote a book about the events.

D The climber George Mallory wanted to be the first person to climb Everest in 1924. He never returned, but no one knows if he reached the top. As a result, there are many books about this famous mountaineering mystery.

E While the explorer Ernest Shackleton was sailing around Antarctica, his ship, *Endurance*, became stuck in the ice. Eventually, Shackleton and his crew left the ship and they spent sixteen days crossing 1,300 kilometres of ocean in small boats to the island of South Georgia. Shackleton published his famous story of survival in 1919.

1 This story isn't about any mountains.

2 The people in the story were not explorers or mountaineers.

3 We don't know if this person achieved his aim.

4 Weather was the problem in this story.

5 The leaders of the teams survived in these stories.

6 These stories include problems with transport.

7 This story became a film.

8 These stories describe long journeys.

Grammar past continuous and past simple

4 Underline any past continuous forms in the article on page 30.

5 Write past continuous sentences.

1 sun / shine and people / sunbathe on / beach

2 phone / ring, but I / leave / the house so I didn't answer it

3 we / not / study when the teacher walked in

4 we / walk past the building when the fire started

5 she / not / think / about her exam results when the envelope arrived

6 it / not / rain, / so we went for a picnic

6 Choose the correct options to complete the conversations.

Conversation one

A: ¹ *Did you see / Were you seeing* all those police cars this morning?

B: No. Where were they?

A: They ² *followed / were following* a red sports car, but I don't know if they caught him.

B: I ³ *saw / was seeing* on the news that there was a bank robbery, so it was probably something to do with that.

A: I can't believe you ⁴ *didn't hear / weren't hearing* them as they went past.

B: I ⁵ *listened / was listening* to music with my headphones on, so I couldn't hear anything else.

Conversation two

A: ⁶ *Did you have / Were you having* a bad journey?

B: No, not too bad. My normal train ⁷ *didn't arrive / wasn't arriving* today, so I had to wait for the later train.

A: So you were fifteen minutes late.

B: Sorry. Yes, I was. Why? ⁸ *Did you wait / Were you waiting* for me?

A: No, but you were late yesterday. And the day before! It's becoming a problem.

Word focus *fall*

7 Look at the forms of the word *fall* in the sentences. Match the sentences (1–5) with the uses and meanings of *fall* (a–e).

1 When did you fall in love with each other?

2 When I learned to ride a bicycle, I fell off it lots of times.

3 My grandfather often falls asleep after lunch.

4 The price of petrol fell again today.

5 The falls are on the other side of this mountain.

a to decrease

b to move down to the ground, by accident

c suddenly have strong feelings for someone

d a place where water moves down from high to low

e to go to sleep

8 Complete these sentences with the missing phrases.

> fell asleep   fell by 3%   fell off   fell in love

1 I met my husband in 1998 and we _____ straight away.

2 The cost of petrol _____ this month.

3 My leg hurts! I _____ my skateboard.

4 We all _____ while we were watching golf on TV.

4c Different challenges

1 Vocabulary extra challenges

You are going to listen to an interview with a conservationist. Before you listen, match the words (1–8) with the definitions (a–g). Two words mean the same thing and match one definition.

1	conservationist	5	jungle
2	rainforest	6	meditation
3	expedition	7	determination
4	preparation	8	mental

a a long journey to find or study something

b quiet thinking to help you relax

c an area of trees in a tropical region (e.g. the Amazon)

d when you don't let anything stop you from achieving your aim

e person who works to protect the environment

f in the mind (e.g. opposite of *physical*)

g the period when you plan something

Listening a walk through the Amazon rainforest

2 🔊 **25** Listen to an interview with Daniel Fanning, the leader of an expedition through the Amazon rainforest. Which of the topics (1–6) does he talk about?

1 how to survive in the rainforest

2 how to prepare for the rainforest

3 what personal qualities you need

4 what you need to carry

5 dangerous animals in the rainforest

6 the physical and mental sides of walking long distances

3 🔊 **25** Listen again. Answer the questions.

1 What was Daniel's job on the expedition?

2 Why did he need to test the equipment and tents?

3 Why didn't he carry much clothing?

4 What are the most important things to carry?

5 How many kilos did he lose?

6 What personal quality does he think you need on this kind of expedition?

Grammar extra *in*, *on* or *at*

> ▶ **GRAMMAR *in, on, at***
> • We use *in* with months, years, seasons and times of the day: *in February, in 1963, in the spring, in the afternoon.*
> • We use *on* with days and dates: *on Saturday, on 29 June.*
> • We use *at* with times and certain time expressions: *at 2 p.m., at the weekend.*

4 Complete the sentences with *in*, *on*, *at* or – (no preposition).

1 _____ May 1953, Edmund Hillary and Tenzing Norgay became the first men to reach the summit of Mount Everest.

2 _____ the evenings, we cooked dinner over a fire and watched the stars.

3 There's another train _____ five minutes. We can catch that one.

4 The two women reached the summit _____ exactly three o'clock that afternoon.

5 The expedition leaves _____ Monday.

6 The rescue team arrived _____ three days later.

7 Roald Amundsen was the first explorer to reach both the North and South Poles, but he died in a plane crash _____ June 18, 1928.

8 The two climbers returned safe and well _____ yesterday.

9 The group of explorers arrived home _____ New Year's Eve.

4d True stories

Listening a true story

1 🎵 **26** Listen to a true story about Yossi Ghinsberg's journey through the jungle of Bolivia. Number the events (a–f) in the correct order (1–6).

a   The men got lost.
b   Yossi was lost in the jungle for three weeks.
c   Yossi travelled on a raft down the river with Kevin.
d   Yossi fell off the raft.
e   Four men travelled into the jungle of Bolivia.
f   Local people found Kevin.

> **Glossary**
> **raft** (n) /rɑːft/ a simple flat boat made with long pieces of wood

2   Dictation Yossi Ghinsberg

🎵 **26** Listen again and complete the story with the words you hear.

¹ _____, Yossi Ghinsberg started a journey with three other men. They were travelling through the jungle of Bolivia but, ² _____, they were lost. ³ _____, two of the group, Yossi and Kevin, built a raft so they could travel down the river and find help.

⁴ _____ they travelled down the river, but ⁵ _____ they hit a rock. Yossi fell off the raft and swam to the shore.

⁶ _____ Yossi was lost in the jungle, his friend Kevin was luckier. He stayed on the raft and ⁷ _____ some local men found him. ⁸ _____ they searched for Yossi and, ⁹ _____, ¹⁰ _____ they found him alive. ¹¹ _____, the other two men never returned.

Real life telling a story

3 Look at the words and phrases (1–11) you wrote in Exercise 2. Match them with the uses (a–e).

a   refers to days and periods of time: _____, _____, _____, _____,
b   sequences parts of the story: _____, _____,
c   introduces new and surprising information: _____,
d   introduces good news: _____
e   introduces bad news: _____

4   Pronunciation intonation for responding

a 🎵 **27** Listen to these phrases. Some speakers sound interested and surprised. Other speakers don't sound interested. Tick the phrases with interested or surprised intonation.

1   Why was that?
2   That was a good idea!
3   Oh no!
4   That was lucky!
5   Wow!

b 🎵 **28** Listen to the sentences again. This time the speakers all sound interested or surprised. Repeat the sentences, copying the intonation.

5   Listen and respond responding to good and bad news

🎵 **29** Listen to someone telling you a story. Respond to the good or bad news with a response from the box. Then compare your response each time with the model answer that follows.

> Why?   That was a good idea!
> Oh no!   Wow!   That was lucky!

> I had a terrible journey into work this morning.

> Why?

4e A story of survival

1 Writing skill structure your writing

a Read the story. The parts of the story (A–E) are in the wrong order. Number the parts in order (1–5).

> **A** ....
> I felt confident when I started walking early on the first day. I had a tent and food and water for three days. Unfortunately, towards the end of day one I lost the trail. Also, the battery on my phone ran out, so I couldn't read the map.

> **B** ....
> I slept for another night, then I got up early on day three before the sun became too hot. Around midday I was feeling dehydrated, but just as I was starting to panic, I came to the edge of a cliff and there at the bottom was the Verde River.

> **C** ....
> It was a beautiful day and I was on a trip though the Sycamore Wilderness Canyon in Arizona. It's an amazing area, and the second largest canyon in the USA (only the Grand Canyon is bigger). Fortunately, it isn't very well known – there are no roads and no campsites, and sometimes you don't see another person for days.

> **D** ....
> It took two hours to climb down the side of the cliff, but eventually I reached the river and drank the water. Further along the river, I found a trail. A day later, I arrived home and I knew I was very lucky to be alive.

> **E** ....
> After one or two hours I was still lost and it was getting dark, so I put up my tent. Luckily it was a clear night and it didn't rain but I didn't sleep very well because I was worried. The next day I walked for hours again in high temperatures and I had hardly any water left.

b Cover the story. Match the time expressions (1–8) with the events (a–h). Then read the story again and check your answers.

1. On the first day
2. Towards the end of day one
3. After one or two hours
4. The next day
5. On day three
6. Around midday
7. It took two hours
8. A day later

a. he arrived home
b. he started walking
c. he was feeling dehydrated
d. to climb down the cliff
e. he lost the trail
f. he was still lost and it was getting dark
g. he walked for hours
h. he got up early

2 Grammar extra adverbs for structure

a Underline these adverbs in the story and notice their position.

> also   only   again   still   just   then

b Write the adverb in the correct place in the sentence.

1. We walked for three hours, and we sat and enjoyed the view. (then)
2. I arrived home as the sun went down. (just)
3. The explorers tried to leave their camp, but the weather was still too bad. (again)
4. After three hours we were lost. (still)
5. We were three days from anywhere, but we had food and water for one more day. (only)
6. The jungle is hot. There are many dangerous animals. (also)

Writing a short story

3 Write a short story (100 words) which begins with the words: 'We only had food and water for one more day …'. In your story, use six or more adverbs.

Wordbuilding verbs and nouns

1 Complete the sentences with these nouns.

achievement   answer   memory   player
score   solution   study   test

1 My biggest _____ was receiving a degree from the university.
2 My father works from home in his _____ .
3 The _____ with number 10 on his shirt is amazing. What's his name?
4 We spent hours looking at the problem but we never found a _____ .
5 What's the _____ to this question?
6 I can't go out tonight. I need to revise for my _____ tomorrow.
7 I have a terrible _____ for people's names. I never remember them.
8 The _____ is two one and there's only five minutes left in the match.

2 Complete these sentences with verbs formed from the nouns in Exercise 1.

1 Good morning class. Today I want to _____ you on the past simple.
2 I can't _____ this puzzle in the newspaper. It's too difficult.
3 Did you _____ 100% on the test?
4 How did you _____ every word on the list? I forgot lots of them.
5 It's easier to learn to _____ a musical instrument when you are young than when you are older.
6 A: Samuel got a grade A in the test.
  B: How did he _____ that?

Learning skills planning your study time

3 Many people learn English with a class of other people. Having regular lessons at a certain time helps you learn but it's also important to study outside the classroom. Think about how you can plan your time for studying on your own. Choose the correct options to make these statements true for you.

HOW I STUDY

1 My favourite time of day for studying is *in the morning / in the afternoon / in the evening.*
2 I think I can spend *about an hour / between two and three hours / more than three hours* a week studying on my own.
3 The best days in my week to study on are *Monday / Tuesday / Wednesday / Thursday / Friday / Saturday / Sunday.*
4 The best place for me to study is *in a particular place in my house / outside my house / in a room at the language school / other.*

4 Now think about these other suggestions for studying. Answer the questions for you.

5 This workbook is an important part of studying. How much of this workbook can you complete every week?
6 It is useful to read through the Student's Book and your notes after each lesson. When will you be able to do this?
7 Most people agree that it is better to study every day for ten or fifteen minutes than once a week for an hour or two. Is it possible for you to work this way? When could you spend a few minutes studying every day (e.g. on the bus to work or during your lunch break)?

Check!

5 Can you remember what you read or heard about these places? Try to answer the questions. You can find the answers in Unit 4 of the Student's Book.

1 Who was in these places in Unit 4 of the Student's Book?

Lukla   Kabul   Tehran
Siula Grande   Atafu

2 What happened to the person or people in these places?

Unit 5 The environment

5a Recycling begins at home

Vocabulary recycling

cling film

1 Look at these notes from a student's vocabulary notebook. Complete the rest of the diagram in the same way.

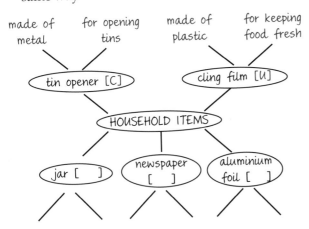

Grammar quantifiers

2 Look at the nouns and decide if you can use *a, an* or *some*.

1	.... banana	5	.... egg
2	.... juice	6	.... milk
3	.... box	7	.... coffee
4	.... can	8	.... carton

> ▶ **SPELL CHECK plural countable nouns**
>
> • With countable nouns, you usually add *-s*:
>   *egg → eggs*
> • Add *-es* to nouns ending in *-ch, -s, -ss, -sh* and *-x*:
>   *sandwich → sandwiches*
> • Change nouns ending in *-y* (after a consonant) to
>   *-i* and add *-es*: *city → cities*
> • Don't change the *-y* to *-i* after a vowel: *key → keys*
> • Some nouns are irregular: *man → men*

3 Look at the spell check box. Then write the plural form of these countable nouns. Use a dictionary if necessary.

1 jar ....
2 bus ....
3 country ....
4 holiday ....
5 woman ....
6 can ....
7 box ....
8 child ....
9 phone ....
10 class ....
11 story ....
12 cartridge ....

4 Complete the pairs of sentences with the quantifiers.

1 some / any
   a There are .... cakes on the table.
   b There isn't .... sugar left.

2 some / much
   a There isn't .... milk left.
   b Don't worry, there's .... more in the fridge.

3 any / many
   a I don't have .... eggs but I can give you one.
   b I don't have .... eggs. We'll have to buy some.

4 a lot of / much
   a We've got .... old aluminium foil we should recycle.
   b We don't use .... aluminium foil because cling film is better.

5 a few / a little
   a There are .... ink cartridges in that box.
   b There's only .... ink in this pen.

6 a few / many
   a I don't get .... days off for holidays.
   b I have .... days off every year for holidays.

7 a little / much
   a I only get .... exercise at the gym each week.
   b Do you get .... exercise?

5 Complete the sentences with these words. Are the sentences true for you?

| any | few | lot | many | ~~some~~ |

1 There are ___*some*___ recycling bins in each office.
2 There aren't _____ plastic cups. Everyone has to bring in their own coffee cup.
3 There are a _____ signs in the offices to remind people to switch off anything electrical at the end of the day.
4 Some people drive to work but there aren't _____ places to park. Most people travel by bus or they cycle to work.
5 We try to reuse a _____ of our paper as well as recycling it.

Reading reusing household items

6 Read the article about recycling. Match the headings (a–e) with the paragraphs (1–5).

a Items made of paper
b Items to put things in
c Plastic bags
d House cleaning
e Clothing

7 Read the article again. Answer these questions.

1 What is better than recycling household items?

2 What can you use for cleaning instead of paper towels?

3 What types of storage items are good for reusing?

4 What three uses does the writer suggest for old newspapers?

5 How can you keep your plants warm in the winter?

6 What two uses does the writer suggest for old plastic bags?

♻ Recycling

Reusing household items is better for the environment than throwing them away or recycling them. Reusing needs less energy than collecting household rubbish or taking it to the recycling centre. Here are some ideas for reusing common items in your house.

1 The next time you don't have any paper towels for cleaning, don't go to the shop. Make your own from old cotton shirts, old socks and old towels. You can clean your car with them, wash the kitchen floor and dust the furniture. And they're cheap!

2 Wash your glass jars and reuse them to keep small items. In the kitchen, you can store beans, tea and spices in them. You can also wash yoghurt pots and other plastic containers and reuse them for food in the fridge.

3 Use your magazines and newspaper for wrapping presents or protecting fragile objects. Before you throw away the paper from your desk, ask yourself: *Can I write on the other side first?* And if you shred paper and newspaper, it makes good compost.

4 Obviously, when your child's old shirt and trousers are too small, you can pass them on to smaller kids. Most countries also have second-hand shops so you can take your shoes and clothes there. But you can also wrap old clothing around the plants in your garden in a cold winter.

5 We all use too many of these every day and they are hard to recycle, so reuse them for carrying your shopping. When you travel, you can put bottles of liquid in them in case they open.

Glossary

compost (n) /ˈkɒmpɒst/ a mixture of dead plants and vegetables we use to grow plants

5b What we consume

Vocabulary results and figures

1 Look at the pie and bar charts. Complete the phrases with these words.

| exactly | just over | nearly | well over |

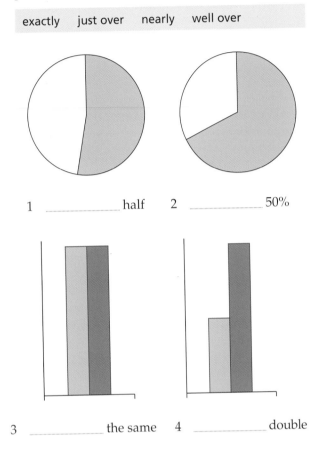

1 _____ half   2 _____ 50%

3 _____ the same   4 _____ double

2 Read the phrases and shade the pie charts.

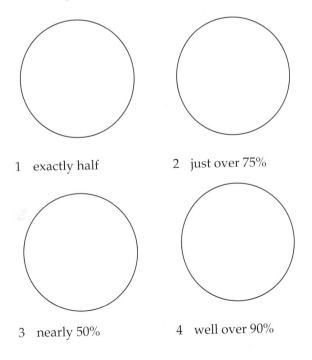

1 exactly half   2 just over 75%

3 nearly 50%   4 well over 90%

Reading understanding a chart

3 This chart compares how often people in different countries recycled their household materials in 2008 and 2009. Complete the statements (1–8) with the correct nationality.

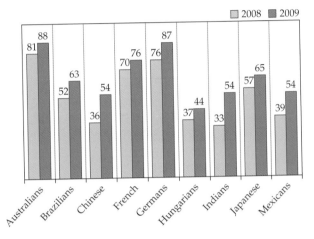

1 In both years, the *Australians* recycled over eighty per cent of the time.
2 The _____ increased their recycling to over three quarters of the time.
3 In 2008, the _____ recycled exactly a third of the time. In 2009, they recycled just over fifty per cent of the time.
4 In 2009, the _____, the _____ and the _____ all recycled at the same frequency.
5 In 2008, the _____ and the _____ recycled over fifty per cent of the time and over sixty a year later.
6 The _____ increased their rate of recycling by exactly fifty per cent.
7 The _____ recycled just over seventy five per cent of the time in 2008 and then well over eighty per cent in 2009.
8 The _____ recycled just over a third of the time in 2008 and over forty per cent in 2009.

Listening managing the environment

4 🔊 **30** Listen to a news report about environmentally-friendly houses. Number the photos (A–C) in the order the speaker talks about them.

> **Glossary**
>
> **carbon emissions** (n) /'kɑː(r)bən ɪ'mɪʃ(ə)nz/ the amount of carbon dioxide that transport or industries put into the air
>
> **climate change** (n) /'klaɪmət tʃeɪndʒ/ changes in the environment and the weather

A

B

C

5 🎵 **30** Listen again and complete these sentences from the news report.

1 It's estimated that the building industry produces around _____ of the world's carbon emissions.

2 The world population is growing, so _____ need houses.

3 The house from Holland is made from _____ and you can buy it in boxes.

4 It takes about _____ to build it.

5 Some people are trying to build houses out of _____, though it isn't a new idea.

6 In _____ a man called Tom Kelly built a house made with _____ glass bottles.

7 In _____, one hotel has covered a wall with more than _____.

8 Two towers in Milan will have _____ on the sides which will improve Milan's _____.

9 The forests also protect the people living there from the _____ of the city.

Grammar articles

6 Complete the sentences with *the, a, an* or – (no article)

1 I love _____ pizzas!

2 One day I'd love to visit _____ Amazon rainforest.

3 _____ New Zealand is a country with every type of natural feature.

4 _____ Maldives are a group of islands in the Indian Ocean.

5 The city has built _____ new wall along the river. The wall will stop flooding in the future.

6 My favourite Hollywood actor is staying at _____ Astoria Hotel in London.

7 I don't like driving at _____ night.

8 One of _____ best holidays I had was staying at home for a week!

9 My father is _____ environmental manager.

10 Do you also speak _____ English at home with your family?

11 What are you doing at _____ weekend? Would you like to go to the beach?

12 A: There's a strange car outside our house!
    B: It's _____ same one I told you about earlier.

7 Pronunciation /ðə/ or /ði:/

🎵 **31** Listen to the sentences in Exercise 6 with *the*. Do you hear the pronunciation /ðə/ or /ði:/?

/ðə/ Sentences: _____

/ði:/ Sentences: _____

8 Read this article. An article (*a/an* or *the*) is missing in nine places. Write in the missing article.

Over three hundred million people live in ∧ United States of America. It is world's most multi-cultural country. It was part of United Kingdom, but it became new country in 1776. Washington DC became capital city and the President still lives in White House today. However, it isn't biggest city. New York is bigger city and it's also more popular with tourists. In particular, they come to see Statue of Liberty.

5c Rubbish we produce

Word focus *take*

1 Replace *take* in the sentences with the correct form of one of these verbs or phrases.

> be careful   carry   drink   ~~go by~~
> go for   have   last   slow down

1 Let's **take a** taxi. It's much faster.   *go by*
2 Would you like to **take** a walk?   ....
3 The journey will **take** about three hours.
   ....
4 **Take your time**! There's no hurry.   ....
5 It's time for you all to **take** a break.   ....
6 You need to **take care** in the jungle. There are many dangerous animals.   ....
7 You need to **take** 10 ml of this medicine twice a day for two weeks.   ....
8 This boat can **take** up to 30 people.   ....

2 Complete the sentences in your own words.

1 I usually take .... when I go to work.
2 The journey to my work takes ....
3 I normally take a break ....
4 It's important to take your time when you
   ....
5 It's important to take care when you
   ....

Listening **one household's rubbish**

3 🔊 **32** Listen to a news report. Answer these questions.

1 What type of news is it about?
   ....
2 Which country is it about?
   ....
3 What examples of electronic devices does it mention?
   ....
4 Does the reporter think recycling electronic devices could have a big effect?
   ....
5 What kind of recycling has become successful in this country?
   ....

4 🔊 **32** Listen again. Complete the factsheet with numbers.

Average households		
1	Total amount of rubbish produced = ... billion kilos	
2	Amount recycled or composted = ... billion kilos	
Electronic devices		
3	The average household owns .... electronic devices.	
4	Households with three or more people own as many as .... devices.	
5	Smaller households own about .... devices.	
6	One million mobile phones could produce .... kilos of gold.	
Paper recycling		
7	Average amount of paper recycled was .... kilos per person or .... kilos per household.	
8	.... % of households can recycle paper.	

By Karyn Maier, Demand Media

Glossary
trash (n) /træʃ/ (AmEng) rubbish

5d Online shopping

Listening an order by phone

1 🔊 **33** Listen to a customer ordering a garden composter by phone. Complete the order form.

Item number: ¹ ....
Name of item: *Garden Composter*
Price: ² .... (including delivery)
Surname of customer: ³ ....
Address: ⁴ .... *Windmill Avenue, Oxford*
Type of credit card: ⁵ ....
Card number: ⁶ ....
Email: ⁷ ....

Real life phoning about an order

2 🔊 **33** Complete the conversation from Exercise 1 with the questions (a–i). Then listen again and check your answers.

a   Can I take your surname?
b   Does that include delivery?
c   Do you have the item number?
d   Can I help you?
e   Would you like confirmation by email?
f   Is that the garden composter?
g   Which credit card would you like to pay with?
h   Can I put you on hold for a moment?
i   Is there anything else I can help you with today?

S = Sales assistant, C = Customer
S: Good morning. ¹ ....
C: Hi, I'm calling about a product on your website. I'd like to order it but the website won't let me.
S: One moment … ² ....
C: Yes, it's 7786-P
S: So, that's 7786-P. OK. ³ ....
C: Yes, that's right.
S: Well, I can take your order by phone.
C: OK, but how much does it cost?
S: Hmm. ⁴ ....
C: Sure.

S: Hello?
C: Yes, hello.
S: Hi, it's £22.
C: ⁵ ....
S: Yes, it does.
C: OK. I'll order it.
S: Right. I'll need to take some details. ⁶ ....
C: It's Bruce. B-R-U-C-E.
S: And the address?
C: 31 Windmill Avenue. And that's in Oxford.
S: ⁷ ....
C: VISA, and the number is 4456 8938 9604 9500.
S: Sorry, is that 9500 at the end?
C: Yes, that's right.
S: ⁸ ....
C: Yes, please. My email is bob dot bruce fifty-one at email dot com.
S: Let me check: bob dot bruce fifty-one at email dot com.
C: That's right.
S: ⁹ ....
C: No, thanks. That's everything.
S: OK. Goodbye.
C: Bye.

3 Listen and respond making an order

🔊 **34** You are ordering an item by phone. Listen and respond to the sales person using this information and your own details. Spell your surname and email address.

Name of item: Laptop
Item number: GR897-01
Type of credit card: Mastercard
Card number: 7558 6799 3647 1023

4 Pronunciation sounding friendly

🔊 **35** Listen to the sales person again. Repeat the expressions with similar intonation so that you sound polite and friendly.

1   Can I help you?
2   Do you have the item number?
3   Can I take your surname?
4   Which credit card would you like to pay with?
5   Can I take the card number?
6   Would you like confirmation by email?
7   Can I have your email address?
8   Is there anything else I can help you with today?

5e Emails about an order

1 Writing skill formal words

These sentences are from two emails. One email is more formal than the other. Write the sentences in the correct order in the two emails

a   Please email this as soon as possible.
b   I'm happy to send you the running shoes.
c   But you didn't give me the item no. ☹
d   Thanks for placing another order with us!
e   We are grateful for your order dated 30th August.
f   Please send asap.
g   We would be delighted to send you the dress immediately.
h   However, we require the correct order number.

Hi Hans!

1   ....
    ....
2   ....
    ....
3   ....
    ....
4   ....
    ....

All the best
Malcolm

Dear Ms Powell

5   ....
    ....
6   ....
    ....
7   ....
    ....
8   ....

Malcolm Douglas
Customer Care Dept.

---

2 Replace the words in bold in the sentences with these more formal words.

apologize	'd be delighted	assistance	inform
provide	receive	refund	request
require	~~would like~~		

1   I **want** to **tell** you about your order. _would like_ ,
    ....

2   I**'m happy** to deliver it today. ....

3   We didn't **get** our order. ....

4   I'm writing to **ask for** a replacement. ....

5   We**'re sorry** for any delay. ....

6   Please **give** your email address. ....

7   When will you **give back** the money?
    ....

8   Do you **need** any **help**? .... ,
    ....

Writing emails

3 Write three different emails between a customer and an online DVD supplier. Follow the instructions in brackets.

Email 1

(1 Request information about a DVD)
    ....
(2 Ask about the price)
    ....
(3 Request information asap)
    ....

Email 2

(4 Thank customer for enquiry)
    ....
(5 Say the price is $10)
    ....
(6 Add that delivery is included in price)
    ....

Email 3

(7 Thank the other person for replying)
    ....
(8 Confirm you want to order it)
    ....
(9 Ask for information on how to pay)
    ....

Wordbuilding hyphenated words

> ▶ **WORDBUILDING hyphenated words**
>
> We sometimes use a hyphen to join two or more words. It's always useful to check in your dictionary but here are some examples of when we use a hyphen:
> * two or more words as a noun, e.g. *e-rubbish, brother-in-law*
> * two or more words as an adjective before a noun, e.g. *out-of-date, second-hand*
> * with a capitalized word, e.g. *anti-English, pro-American*
> * with numbers, fractions and measurements, e.g. *twenty-one, two-thirds, three-litre plastic bottle, five-star hotel*

1 Look at the wordbuilding box. Then write the missing hyphens in these sentences.

1 Please board the plane as we are ready for take off.
2 There's some out of date chicken here, I'll have to throw it away.
3 A lot of people are pro European.
4 Nearly three quarters of the population regularly recycles glass.
5 I only use eco friendly washing detergent. It's better for the environment.
6 Do you have an up to date bus timetable?
7 My birthday is on the thirty first of January.
8 My wife's mother is my mother in law.
9 A marathon is a twenty six mile run. That's forty two kilometres.
10 All our products use state of the art technology.

2 Look at an English text (for example in a newspaper, on the internet or in the Student's Book) and circle more examples of hyphenated words.

Learning skills using a dictionary (2)

3 Use these exercises to practise your dictionary skills.

1 Look at the noun in this dictionary extract. Is it countable or uncountable? How do you know from the dictionary extract?

> **information** /ˌɪnfəˈmeɪʃən/ noun [U] knowledge or facts about a person or thing

2 Find these four nouns in your dictionary. Are they countable, uncountable or both?

> foot   information   luggage   time   tooth

3 These words all have two or more parts. Find them in your dictionary. Which part of the word or phrase did you look for first?

> out-of-date   eco-friendly   recycling bin
> tin opener   user-friendly

4 Find the verb *take* in your dictionary. Answer the questions.
  a How many different meanings does the word *take* have: fewer than 10? between 10 and 20? more than 20?
  b Find a new collocation or expression with the word *take*.

5 Look up the word *reuse* in your dictionary. From the definition, guess the meaning of the prefix *re-*. Then check your answer by looking up the definition of *re-* in your dictionary.

Check!

4 What is the connection between these pairs of words from Unit 5 of the Student's Book? Check your ideas by looking back through the unit.

1 Earth ⟷ 30%

2 computers ⟷ gold

3 a few ⟷ a little

4 tell ⟷ inform

5 Great Wall ⟷ Green Wall

6 Plastiki ⟷ plastic bottles

7 Pacific Ocean ⟷ Garbage Patch

8 toxic ⟷ poisonous

9 Senegal ⟷ Djibouti

10 Atacama ⟷ Chile

6a A new life in paradise

1 Vocabulary extra life events

Match the words in A with the phrases in B. Then complete the sentences.

A	buy	get	go	leave	start	retire

B	a family	their first home	from work
	my driving licence	home	to university

1 I'll _____ when I'm eighteen. I want to study physics.

2 Young people in my country usually _____ and share a flat with friends as soon as they finish school.

3 It's difficult for young people to _____ nowadays because prices are so high.

4 If I _____, my parents are going to buy me a car!

5 Most people _____ in their mid-sixties but I plan to in my mid-fifties. That's why I'm saving money now.

6 We decided to _____ once we'd bought a house. Our first child was a girl.

Reading building a dream house

2 Read the article. Match the headings (A–D) with the paragraphs (1–4).

A Preparations before building
B The dream
C With help from their friends
D The obvious choice

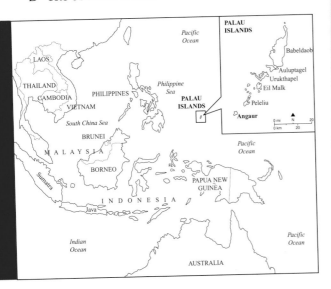

A new life in paradise

Alex Sheshunoff is a writer and Sarah Kalish was a lawyer. They both had good jobs and an apartment in Iowa city. However, one day they decided to leave it all behind and build a new home for themselves. Most people would be happy to look locally, perhaps in the nicer neighbourhoods, but Alex and Sarah planned to find a place in paradise to create their new home.

For Alex, it was fairly easy to choose an island with everything he wanted. As a keen scuba diver, Alex first visited the Palau group of islands years ago because of the beautiful ocean. He continued to go back there from time to time, so this seemed like a good choice. The islands are about 7,500 kilometres west of Hawaii and they are difficult to reach. However, they have green forests with interesting wildlife and they are surrounded by a blue ocean full of colourful fish. In the end, Alex and Sarah chose one island in particular – Angaur.

Angaur is only thirteen kilometres around, with a population of about 150 people. Before Alex and Sarah could start to work on building a house, they had to get permission from the head of the island – an 83-year-old woman. She was worried they intended to develop the area for other tourists, but Alex explained that they just wanted to build a simple house. They agreed on the rent of $100 a month for twenty years. The head of the island was happy. She said, 'Angaur welcomes you.'

Then the real work began. Alex and Sarah didn't want to pay for a construction company, so they taught themselves a lot about building. A lot of their friends from Iowa came out to help. In return they got a free holiday by the beach. The local people of Angaur also worked for the couple and after many months of hard work and a final visit from the head of the island, their dream house was ready.

3 Read the article again. Answer the questions.

1 Where does the writer think most people would plan to build a new house?

2 Why was it easy for Alex to choose a location?

3 How far are the islands from Hawaii?

4 What are the good things about the islands?

5 How many people live on Angaur?

6 Who gave them permission to build the house?

7 How much was their rent per month?

8 What did their friends get in return for helping?

9 Who visited the house when it was built?

Grammar verb patterns with *to* + infinitive

4 Underline examples of *to* + infinitive in the article in Exercise 2.

5 Match the beginnings of the sentences (1–8) with the endings (a–h).

1 Turn the key
2 For dinner they plan
3 Save your money
4 Use a dictionary
5 Go to Egypt
6 For our holidays, we intend
7 Go to university
8 At the bank, I want

a to find the translation.
b to take us to a restaurant.
c to go camping.
d to unlock the door.
e to see the pyramids.
f to have enough for a holiday.
g to take out some money.
h to get a degree.

6 Look at the example. Then complete the conversation with these pairs of words.

afraid / move	difficult / keep	easy / make
great / live	nice / see	sad / see

A: Hi. It's [1] _____*nice to see*_____ you again after all these years. It's been such a long time.
B: Yes, it has. But it's really [2] _____ in contact with everyone.
A: Yes, it is. And we were so [3] _____ you leave. Remind me. Where did you move to?
B: Australia. We moved there five years ago.
A: Really? Five years ago! I'd be [4] _____ such a long way from my friends and family.
B: In fact, it was [5] _____ new friends. We're very happy there. And it's [6] _____ in a hot country with beaches and a beautiful coast.

7 Choose the correct verb form to complete the sentences.
1 I'm happy *help / to help / helping* you with your homework.
2 You can't *throw / to throw / throwing* the ball forwards in rugby.
3 We want *meet / to meet / meeting* at six o'clock.
4 Are you good at *play / to play / playing* tennis?
5 Do you feel like *go / to go / going* out later?
6 I'm studying Chinese *get / to get / getting* a job in Beijing.

8 Pronunciation sentence stress

🔊 **36** Listen to these sentences. Then practise saying them. Stress the underlined words.

1 <u>Pleased</u> to <u>meet</u> you.
2 <u>Nice</u> to <u>see</u> you.
3 It's <u>lovely</u> to <u>be</u> here.

9 Complete these sentences in your own words.
1 I'm always happy to _____.
2 It's hard to _____.
3 I think people are crazy to _____.

6b Special occasions

Vocabulary celebrations

1 Complete the text about different festivals with these words.

bands	candles	costumes	fireworks
floats	masks	parades	

Festivals around the world

St Patrick's Day

On 17th March, Ireland celebrates Saint Patrick's Day. There are ¹ _____ down the streets and people ride on ² _____ .

Maskarra Festival

Every October in Bacolod City in the Philippines, thousands of people go to the Maskarra festival wearing ³ _____ and ⁴ _____ .

Bonfire Night

On 5th November in the United Kingdom, people light fires and let off lots of ⁵ _____ into the night sky.

Santa Lucia Day

On 13th December, Swedish people celebrate the festival of Santa Lucia. Traditionally, girls wear white dresses and a crown with ⁶ _____ . In the past they lit them, but nowadays they don't.

Teuila Festival

This festival in Western Samoa lasts two weeks. There are colourful decorations hanging in the streets and ⁷ _____ playing music everywhere you go.

Listening planning a celebration

2 🎵 **37** Listen to a group of people planning a party. Choose the correct option (a–c) to answer the questions.

1 What is the reason for the party?
  a a birthday
  b an anniversary
  c a retirement

2 Where do they decide to celebrate the party?
  a in the office
  b at a restaurant
  c at Rosemary's home

3 Who do they plan to invite?
  a only work colleagues
  b family and friends
  c they can't decide

4 What present are they going to buy her?
  a a book on gardening
  b a cake
  c a plant

3 🎵 **37** Listen again. Answer the questions.

1 Why is the meeting secret?

2 Why does one person not want to have the party in the office?

3 Why do they choose Zeno's?

4 What is on the menu there?

5 How many people do they need to book the restaurant for?

6 What time is the party?

7 Why can't one person be there at five o'clock?

8 Why do they choose a particular present for Rosemary?

9 Why do they stop the meeting?

Grammar future forms: *going to, will* and present continuous

4 Choose the correct option to complete part of the conversation from Exercise 2.

C: What time ¹ *will everyone meet / is everyone going to meet* there?

A: Straight after work. At five.

B: But ² *I'll work / I'm working* late on Friday.

A: Well, between five and six then. We also need to get her a present.

C: Oh yes! What ³ *are we giving / are we going to give* her? I know, she loves plants and I think ⁴ *she's going to spend / she's spending* a lot of time gardening when she retires.

A: Good idea. A plant.

C: And I think we should have a special cake as well.

A: ⁵ *Is the restaurant going to make / Will the restaurant make* us one?

C: Erm, I'm not sure. ⁶ *I'm going to / I'll ask* them.

5 Choose the correct response (a–b) for the sentences (1–5).

1 Oh no! I've forgotten my wallet!
   a Don't worry. I'll pay.
   b Don't worry. I'm going to pay.

2 Can you help me later?
   a Sorry, I'll help Max later.
   b Sorry, I'm going to help Max later.

3 Are you in the parade this afternoon?
   a No, I'm not, but I'll watch it at three.
   b No, I'm not, but I'm going to watch it at three.

4 Do you want to come to the nightclub with me this evening?
   a Sorry, but I'll see a film with a friend.
   b Sorry, but I'm going to see a film with a friend.

5 Let's go to the cinema tonight.
   a Good idea. I'll see what's on.
   b Good idea. I'm going to see what's on.

6 Pronunciation contracted forms

🎧 **38** Listen to six sentences. Tick the sentence you hear (a–b).

1 a Don't worry. I'll pay.
   b Don't worry. I will pay.

2 a I'm going to help Max later.
   b I am going to help Max later.

3 a Shelley's coming too.
   b Shelley is coming too.

4 a He'll be eighteen years old tomorrow.
   b He will be eighteen years old tomorrow.

5 a They're going to travel round the world.
   b They are going to travel round the world.

6 a Why aren't you watching the parade?
   b Why are you not watching the parade?

> ▶ **GOING TO or PRESENT CONTINUOUS**
>
> You can often use either form to talk about plans and arrangements in the future, e.g. *We're meeting in the café at five. = We're going to meet in the café at five.*
>
> When you use the present continuous to talk about the future, you normally need a future time reference, e.g. *We're meeting in the café **at five**.*
>
> When you don't use a future time expression, the present continuous often refers to the present time, e.g. *We're meeting in the café (now).*

7 Look at the grammar box. Then read these sentences and decide if you can replace *going to* with the present continuous without changing the future meaning.

1 We're going to meet my friends later today. ✓
   We're meeting my friends later today.

2 We're going to call you back. ✗
   ~~(We're calling you back.)~~

3 Is the teacher going to tell us the answer?

4 Are you going to go to the festival tomorrow?

5 They're going to decorate the float.

6 The parade is going to pass my house this afternoon.

7 I'm going to tell you something I've never told anyone before.

8 Why is everyone going to wear a mask?

8 Dictation plans for a celebration

🎧 **39** Listen to someone describing their plans for a celebration and write their words.

_____

_____

_____

_____

_____

_____

_____

6c Coming of age

Listening an ancient ceremony

1 🎵 **40** Listen to a documentary about a ceremony of the Apache Indians. Number the pictures (1–5) in the order the speaker describes them.

a

b

c

d

e

2 🎵 **40** Listen again. Complete the summary of the ancient ceremony.

An ancient ceremony

The Indian tribe called the Mescalero Apaches have a special ceremony every year. It starts on the
¹ _____ and lasts for four days. It is a ceremony for the young Apache ² _____ .

At the beginning, each family makes food for many guests and the men build a special tepee. The girls will live in this for ³ _____ days. On the first day the girls run towards the ⁴ _____ and round a basket of food four times.

Each time represents the four stages of their life: infant, ⁵ _____ , teenager and adult woman. On the last night, they have to dance for over ⁶ _____ hours. In the morning, the girls come out of the tepee with white clay on their ⁷ _____ . They run and wash the clay off their faces. The tepee falls to the ground. The girls receive a new name and celebrate their new position – as ⁸ _____ .

> **Glossary**
> **clay** (n) /kleɪ/ wet material from the ground which you can use to make bowls, cups and plates.

Word focus *get*

3 Complete the phrases with *get* in the sentences with these words.

back	married	pension	plane	presents
ready	~~up~~			

1 What time do you normally get ___*up*___ in the morning?
2 What time do you get _____ from work?
3 Hurry up and get _____ . It's nearly time to leave.
4 Which gate do we need to get the _____ from?
5 What _____ did you get from everyone for your birthday?
6 In my country you get your _____ when you are 65.
7 We plan to get _____ when we both finish university but it won't be a big wedding.

6d An invitation

Real life inviting, accepting and declining

1 🔊 **41** Listen to two telephone conversations. Answer these questions.

Conversation 1

1 Where has Sonia been recently?

2 When does she want to meet Mihaela?

3 Where are they going to meet?

4 Who does Mihaela want to bring?

Conversation 2

5 What is Philippe going to do?

6 Why does Phillippe decline Mihaela's invitation?

7 What does Mihaela suggest?

8 Does Phillippe accept the invitation in the end?

2 🔊 **41** Complete the extracts from the conversations in Exercise 1 with these expressions. Then listen again and check your answers.

> Do you want   How about   I'd like   I'd love to
> It sounds   That would   It's very nice
> Why don't you   Yes, OK

Conversation 1

Sonia: I'm at work so I can't talk long.
          ¹ _____ to meet after work?
Mihaela: ² _____. Do you mean tonight?
Sonia: Yes. ³ _____ meeting outside my office? We could go to that new Lebanese restaurant on the corner of Main Street.
Mihaela: ⁴ _____ great. Oh, I've just remembered. I have a friend from France staying. He's doing a language course at the college near me.
Sonia: That's OK. ⁵ _____ invite him as well?
Mihaela: ⁶ _____ be great. I'll do that.
Sonia: OK. See you later.

Conversation 2

Mihaela: I'm meeting a close friend of mine tonight and ⁷ _____ to take you to meet her.
Philippe: ⁸ _____ of you to ask, but I'm busy tonight. I have an exam tomorrow so I need to revise at home.
Mihaela: Are you sure? We're going to eat at a new restaurant. We could get home early or you could study first and come out later.
Philippe: Honestly, ⁹ _____ but I'm afraid this exam is really important.
Mihaela: I completely understand. But if you change your mind, give me a call. OK?

3 Listen and respond responding to an invitation

🔊 **42** Listen and respond to two different invitations. For each one, first decline the invitation, and give a reason, then accept it. Compare your responses with the model answer that follows.

> Do you want to go to the cinema tonight?

> Sorry, I can't because I'm going to a football match tonight.

4 Pronunciation emphasizing words

a 🔊 **43** Listen to these sentences. You will hear a speaker saying the sentence in two ways. Which has the most natural sentence stress? Write *1* or *2*.

1 I'm really sorry but I can't. *1*
2 That'd be great.
3 It's so nice of you to ask.
4 I'd love to.
5 It sounds nice.

b Practise saying the sentences.

6e An annual festival

1 Writing skill descriptive adjectives

a Replace the words in bold in the sentences with these more descriptive adjectives.

> colourful   dull   exciting   massive
> miserable   tasty

1 I sat down with the fishermen to eat a **nice** meal of fresh fish from the sea. ....
2 The women were wearing **red, yellow and blue** dresses for the party. ....
3 The parade through the streets was long and a bit **boring** after a while. ....
4 The mountains outside our hotel were **big** and had snow on the top. ....
5 The children didn't seem **unhappy** even though they had very little food. ....
6 The bus journey from my hotel to the centre wasn't very **interesting**. ....

b Match the sentences from Exercise 1a with topics (a–f) in the table.

a clothes	b food
c people	d transport and towns
e festivals	f nature and geographic features

c Imagine you are writing a description which includes the six topics (a–f) in Exercise 1b. Which of these adjectives would be useful for each topic? Write them in the table in Exercise 1b. You can use some adjectives for more than one topic. Use a dictionary to help you.

> amazing   attractive   beautiful   delicious
> dull   enormous   friendly   fun   miserable
> polluted   pretty   smart   speedy
> uncomfortable   unhealthy

d Add one more of your own adjectives to each topic in Exercise 1b.

Writing a description

2 A student has prepared this plan for a description of the annual festival in her town. Use the notes in the plan and write the description. Write one paragraph.

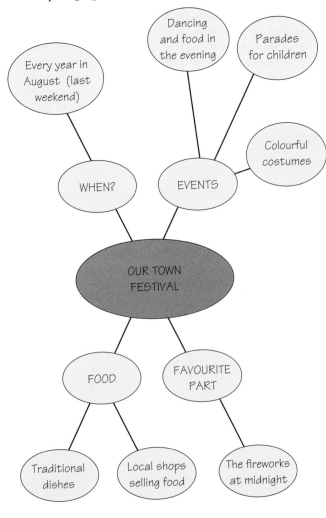

3 Now plan and write a similar short description of an event that happens in your town once a year.

Wordbuilding synonyms

1 Cross out the word in each group which isn't a synonym. Use a dictionary to help you.

1 sorry apologetic ~~afraid~~
2 fast warm speedy
3 scary awful frightening
4 good-looking strong handsome
5 tall thin skinny
6 well-dressed polite smart
7 hide find discover
8 see notice touch
9 needy important essential
10 relaxed happy cheerful

Learning skills assessing your own progress

2 You are now halfway through this course. Think about your progress so far. Answer the questions on the self-assessment questionnaire on the right. After each answer, write a comment to explain your answers.

Check!

3 Look at these words from Unit 6 of the Student's Book. Write the words in the correct place in the table. Circle words that are not English words, but names of things in different languages.

| candle | feijoada | firework | infant | Hamar |
| middle-aged | Port-of-Spain | teenagers | Tremé |

A place	
A type of dish or something you can eat	
Something that gives light	
A stage of life	
A group of people	

Assess your progress

1 How would you describe your progress in English on the course so far?

Excellent ☐   Good ☐
Satisfactory ☐   Not very good ☐

Comment on your answer:
_____
_____
_____

2 Which areas would you like to work on most for the rest of the course?

Speaking ☐   Grammar ☐
Listening ☐   Writing ☐
Pronunciation ☐ Vocabulary ☐
Reading ☐

Comment on your answer:
_____
_____
_____

3 Which types of activities in class do you think are most useful for you?
_____
_____
_____

4 What's one thing you would like more of on this course?
_____
_____

5 What's one thing you would like less of?
_____
_____

6 What question do you have for your teacher about the rest of the course? Write it here and ask your teacher to reply.
_____
_____
_____

Unit 7 Work

7a A changing world

Grammar present perfect and past simple

1 Choose the correct options to complete the text about the discovery of oil in the Canadian province of Alberta.

2 Complete these questions about the article. Use the answers to help you.

1 How long .... ?
For many years.

2 How much .... ?
Billions of dollars.

3 What .... ?
Thousands of new jobs.

4 When .... ?
In the sixties.

5 How .... ?
From farming and hunting.

6 ....
gas or electricity in the sixties?
No, it didn't.

3 Dictation two opinions

44 Two people are giving opinions about the changes in Alberta. Listen and write their words.

Person 1

....

....

....

....

....

Person 2

....

....

....

....

the region ⁴ *has become / became* very wealthy. But the beauty of the local area ⁵ *hasn't survived / didn't survive*. Local resident Jim Boucher remembers the region before the oil. He ⁶ *has been / was* a child here in the sixties. There ⁷ *have been / were* forests and lakes, and people ⁸ *have made / made* a living from farming and hunting. The area ⁹ *hasn't had / didn't have* gas or electricity. Now many of the old forests ¹⁰ *have disappeared / disappeared* and there are mines and new buildings all over the land.

Oil companies ¹ *have been / were* in the area of Fort Mackay in northern Alberta for many years. They ² *have spent / spent* billions of dollars in the last decade in order to build mines and get the oil out of the ground. As a result, the industry ³ *has created / created* thousands of new jobs over the years and

4 Pronunciation irregular past participles

a 🔊 **45** Listen and write these past participle verbs under the correct vowel sound in the table.

bought	brought	come	done
flown	found	grown	run	taught
thought	won

/ɔː/	/ʌ/	/əʊ/	/aʊ/

b 🔊 **46** Listen and check your answers.

Vocabulary jobs

5 Complete the job words in these sentences with *a, e, i, o* and *u*.

1 We arrived late at the hotel but the r_c_pt_ _n_st was very welcoming and helpful.

2 The s_l_s r_pr_s_nt_t_v_ tried to sell everyone something they didn't want.

3 I earned some extra money working in a supermarket as a sh_p _ss_st_nt.

4 She loves clothes and wants to become a f_sh__n d_s_gn_r.

5 I'm studying to be a c_mp_t_r pr_gr_mm_r. I'd also like to create video games one day.

6 Being a p_l_c_ _ff_c_r involves protecting the public.

7 I'm a m_rk_t_ng m_n_g_r and I plan all the advertising for our company.

6 Replace the words in bold in the sentences with these adjectives.

boring	skilled	challenging	physical
dangerous

1 Sometimes being a police officer can be **unsafe** but usually most people are happy to see you.

2 People think accountants have **uninteresting** jobs but I like working with numbers.

3 Designers are highly-**trained** people. They have to study for a long time before they can work.

4 I work in construction. You have to be fit because the work is very **hard on the body**.

5 Managing a group of people can be **difficult, but also interesting**.

Grammar present perfect with *for* and *since*

7 Complete the sentences with the present perfect form of the verbs and *for* or *since*.

1 I _____ (teach) in the same school _____ fifteen years.

2 We _____ (not / fly) anywhere _____ our holiday in Australia.

3 My brother _____ (run) in the New York marathon _____ the last five years.

4 The children _____ (grow) a lot _____ you last saw them.

5 Wow! I _____ (not / see) you _____ nearly twenty years!

6 My family _____ (live) on this island _____ the eighteenth century.

8 Complete the questions. Then answer them in two different ways.

1 How long _____ (you / live) in your current home?
Since _____ . / For _____ .

2 How long _____ (you / know) your best friend?
Since _____ . / For _____ .

3 How long _____ (you / have) this book?
Since _____ . / For _____ .

4 How long _____ (you / be) in your current job?
Since _____ . / For _____ .

9 Grammar extra *been* and *gone*

> ▶ **BEEN** and **GONE**
> • We use the past participle *been* to say someone went somewhere and came back, e.g. *I've been to London (but I'm not there now).*
> • We use the past participle *gone* to say someone went somewhere and is still there, e.g. *He's gone to London (and he's still there now).*

Look at the grammar box. Then complete the sentences with *been* or *gone*.

1 My boss has _____ to the meeting and he's back at his desk now.

2 She's _____ to work and won't be back until this evening.

3 Have you ever _____ to Singapore?

4 I haven't seen Bill today. Where's he _____ ?

5 I haven't seen you for ages! Where have you _____ ?

7b A landscape architect

Reading outdoor design

1 Read the article and answer the questions.

1 What is Drew's job during the day? ....

2 What is his job in the evening? ....

3 Where does he like working in his spare time?

....

2 Read the article again. Answer the questions.

1 When did Drew become interested in the outside world?

....

2 What does a landscape architect do?

....

3 What kind of job is it?

....

4 What does he do during his breaks at work?

....

5 What does his wife help him with?

....

6 When does he work until the early morning?

....

7 What has his latest book won?

....

Drew Aquilina: Landscape architect and environmental cartoonist

Drew Aquilina is a landscape architect. As a child he loved plants and animals and studied nature. Then, later in life, he studied architecture, and now he designs areas outside with trees and flowers.

It's a creative and highly-skilled job and he's very busy, travelling and working in different places. However, he also has another job. He's an environmental cartoonist, and during the day he thinks about his next cartoon.

Drew says, 'When I get a break, I plan a cartooning storyline I want to draw in the evening.'

At the end of the day, he goes home and has dinner with his wife Lisa. They talk about the day and discuss his new ideas for cartoons. Lisa often helps him with ideas for the dialogues. Then in the evening, when most people are relaxing and watching TV, Drew finally sits down and starts work on the cartoons. He often works late in the evening and, if he has lots of ideas, until early in the morning.

Drew's latest book of cartoons, called 'Green Pieces: Green from the Pond Up', has even won a book award. And when he has spare time, what does he do? More work! He loves going outside and working in the garden.

Grammar prepositions of place and movement

3 Complete the sentences with these prepositions of place or movement.

across	down	in	next	on	opposite
through	up				

1 Walk _____ the steps to the café.

2 Get _____ . I'll give you a lift to work.

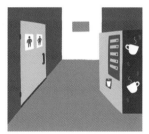

3 The toilets are _____ the coffee machine.

4 Reception is _____ the ground floor.

5 The plant is _____ to the books.

6 Walk _____ the road to the entrance.

7 Go _____ the doors and turn left.

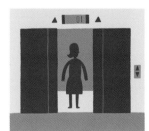

8 Take the lift _____ to the tenth floor.

4 Pronunciation intrusive /w/

a 🔊 **47** Listen to the sentences. Which words have a /w/ sound between them?

1 Go /w/ up the steps.
2 Go through the doors. (*No /w/*)
3 Sue's on the third floor.
4 Sue often works on the third floor.
5 You are on the fifth floor today.
6 You take the lift to the fifth floor.
7 Go in the lift.
8 Get in the lift.
9 Go out of this door.

b 🔊 **47** Listen again and repeat the sentences.

Vocabulary places in a building

5 Read the clues for places in a building and complete the crossword.

Across

2 This is the room or floor below the ground floor.
5 When you walk into the front of a building, you go through the _____ .
8 Go up and down in this.
9 Walk along this to go to different offices.

Down

1 A place to eat at work.
3 When you enter a building, you are on the _____ floor.
4 You work in this room.
6 In an emergency, go out of this kind of door.
7 Don't take the lift. Go up these and get some exercise!

7c Hard work

Vocabulary extra job satisfaction

1 Match these words with the different comments about jobs.

> colleagues   opportunities   pension
> promotion   salary   training

1   My boss wants to meet me tomorrow about moving up into a new job. I'm very excited. ....

2   It isn't as high as I'd like but there are other benefits which make the job good. ....

3   Everyone in my department works hard. We're a great team. ....

4   I love my job because I have so many chances to travel and meet lots of interesting new people. ....

5   Ten per cent of my salary goes into this, so hopefully I can retire early. ....

6   I go away for one week in every year to learn about new developments. ....

Listening talking about jobs

2 🎵 **48** Listen to five people talking about their jobs. Match the people (1–5) with what they say about their jobs (a–f). There is one extra answer.

a   This person enjoys his/her job.
b   This person needs someone for a job.
c   This person describes his/her work.
d   This person wants to work for a new company.
e   This person has just started a new job.
f   This person doesn't like his/her current job.

3 🎵 **48** Listen again and answer the questions.

1   Person 1: Who else is helping to build the dam? ....

2   Person 2: What is this person learning about? ....

3   Person 3: Where does this person want to work instead? ....

4   Person 4: How long has this person worked here? ....

5   Person 5: What does this company usually have to provide? ....

Word focus *make* or *do*

4 Write the words in the table.

> a̶ c̶a̶l̶l̶   a̶ j̶o̶b̶   a mistake   a noise   business
> coffee   dinner   housework   money   well
> work   your bed

make	do
a call	*a job*

5 Complete the sentences with *make* or *do* and words from Exercise 4.

1   How much .... do you .... a month? A thousand dollars?

2   Go outside if you want to .... ! I want to relax and read my book.

3   Can you help me to .... some .... ? There are clothes on the floor and the dishes need washing.

4   I hope you .... in your exams today. Good luck!

5   Would you like me to .... you a cup of .... ?

6   Before you go out, I want you to put everything away in your bedroom and ....

7   Can I borrow your mobile to .... a quick .... to my colleague at work?

8   If I .... a really good .... on this project, my boss says I'll get a pay rise.

7d A job interview

Vocabulary job adverts

1 Complete the two job adverts with these words.

> apply   contact details   CV   description
> essential   position   provide   staff

> We are looking for three restaurant [1] ....
> to work in central London. For a full job
> [2] ...., email info@RDrestaurants.com.
> We will [3] .... training but previous work
> experience as a waiter is also [4] ....

> The Royal Hotel has a new [5] .... for a
> trainee manager. You can [6] .... by
> sending us your [7] .... and [8] ....

Real life a job interview

2 🔊 **49** Listen to two extracts from a job interview.
Answer the questions.

> **Glossary**
> **strength** (n) /streŋθ/ something you are very good at in a job
> **weakness** (n) /ˈwiːknəs/ something you are not good at and
> need to improve

1 What did the person send to the interviewer?

2 What is the position?

3 What is her current job?

4 What are her responsibilities in her current job?

5 Why does she want to change her job?

6 What did she do when her hotel manager was
ill?

7 Give some examples of her strengths.

8 What does she ask the interviewer about?

3 🔊 **49** Match the questions (1–7) with the responses
(a–g). Then listen to the interview again and check
your answers.

1 How long have you worked in your
current position?
2 Why do you want to leave? Why have you
applied for this position?
3 Would you describe yourself as ambitious?
4 Do you work well in a team?
5 Can you give me an example of when you
have worked with other people?
6 What are some of your other strengths?
7 Do you have any questions for me?

a Yes, I suppose I am, a little. Though really, I like
learning new things and working with different
people.
b I work hard and I enjoy working with other
people.
c Yes, I think so.
d Recently, we had a conference at our hotel so
there was lots to arrange. The hotel manager
was very ill that week, so all of us on reception
had to help with everything.
e Well, I like working at the hotel, but I'm more
interested in working for a business like yours.
f Yes, I do. Would I receive any training?
g I've been there for about a year.

4 Listen and respond job interview questions

a Look at the questions from a job interview. Make
some notes about how you would answer each
question.

1 How long have you worked in your current job?
2 Would you describe yourself as ambitious?
3 What are some of your main strengths?
4 Do you have any weaknesses?
5 What's the most difficult thing you have ever
done?
6 How well do you work with other people?
7 Can you give me an example of how you have
solved a problem at work?

b 🔊 **50** Listen to an interviewer and respond to
his questions using your notes. Compare your
responses with the suggested answers.

> How long have you worked
> in your current job?

> I've been there since 2008.

7e Applying for a job

Vocabulary and writing a CV

1 Complete the headings (1–8) in the CV.

Natalie Peltier

¹ **N** .... : French

² **D** .... **of b** .... :   13 June 1991

³ **A** .... : 25 rue Felix Cadras, 62100 Calais

⁴ **E** ....
2010: Degree in restaurant management

⁵ **W** .... **e** ....
Summer 2010: Assistant Manageress of small restaurant in city centre

⁶ **S** ....
Languages: Fluent in English
Computing: Word

⁷ **I** ....
Films and theatre

⁸ **R** ....
Amélie Canaux, (restaurant owner)
51 rue de Marseille, 62100 Calais

2 Writing skill missing out words in CVs

a Complete the sentences from some CVs with the past simple form of these verbs.

advise	assist	design	look after	manage
play	sell	~~teach~~	translate	welcome

1   *Taught*   English to business people.
2   ....   customers about finance.
3   ....   websites for many clients.
4   ....   guests to the hotel and checked them in.
5   ....   young children at a local kindergarten.
6   ....   a department with a team of six.
7   ....   ice cream during the summer.
8   ....   legal documents from German into English.
9   ....   basketball for a student team.
10   ....   the manager of a café and managed it when she was away.

b Read what a student says at a job interview. He describes his education, work history and interests. Rewrite the information for a CV.

> 'I'm studying Geography at University and I'm also learning English at a language school. I worked in a café at weekends and I managed a group of teenagers on a summer camp last year. I've played in two football teams and I like to play the Saxophone.'

Education

1   *studying Geography at University*

2   ....

Hobbies and interests

3   ....

4   ....

Work experience

5   ....

6   ....

Wordbuilding suffixes

1 Write the job words for 1–12 using these suffixes.

-ant -ee -ent -er -ian
-ist -or -r

1 library
2 act
3 music
4 photograph
5 account
6 write
7 electric
8 reception
9 employ
10 manage
11 study
12 paint

2 Tick (✓) the job words with a suffix.

1 doctor ✗
2 shop assistant ✓
3 pilot
4 chef
5 computer programmer
6 engineer
7 editor
8 film star
9 designer
10 security guard
11 police officer
12 journalist

3 Read the definitions and write the job word using a suffix.

1 This person serves tables in a restaurant.
 waiter (or waitress)

2 This person is involved in the arts.

3 This person manages a bank.
4 This person studies geology.
5 This person dances ballet.

6 This person plays a piano.

Learning skills writing a language-learning diary

4 Read the advice for writing a language learning diary.

When you study English (or any other language), it can be useful and interesting to write a language-learning diary. It's similar to a diary about your daily life but you can write about the following things:

- Did you learn something new today? What was it (e.g. new grammar, new vocabulary)?
- How can you try to learn and use this new area of language?
- What did you do in class today? What did you enjoy? What didn't you find helpful?
- How did you feel during the lesson? Did you feel positive or negative about the lesson?

Remember that this language-learning diary is a good way to think about how you learn and it's another way to practise your English!

Check!

5 Read the clues and complete the grid with words from Unit 7 of the Student's Book. The six words give the word for a job.

1 Abbreviation for *curriculum vitae*
2 Often confused with *make*
3 Past participle of *win*
4 Abbreviation for qualification *Bachelor of Science*
5 My office is _____ the third floor.
6 Type of photo showing inside something (e.g. a human body)

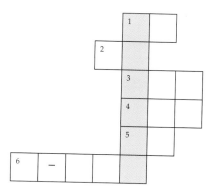

59

Unit 8 Technology

8a Using technology

Vocabulary internet verbs

1 Match these verbs with the groups of words (1–8) to make collocations.

connect to	do	download	log in to
search	set up	subscribe to	write

1 _____ music videos files

2 _____ your online bank account
Facebook your email account

3 _____ a magazine a daily podcast
a blog

4 _____ the web the internet for a pen

5 _____ an email a blog
a computer program

6 _____ an account a tent a company

7 _____ the internet a printer wifi

8 _____ online gaming experiments
work

Listening communication problems

2 🔘 **51** Listen to a conversation between two explorers on an expedition. Answer the questions.

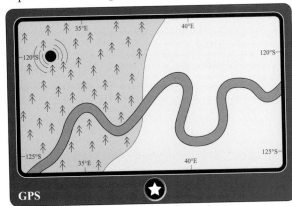

1 What hasn't the person used before?

....

2 Why is there a problem with it?

....

3 What location are they looking for?

....

4 How far away is it?

....

5 Why can't the pilot land nearer to them?

....

6 What needs recharging?

....

3 Dictation technology for explorers

🔘 **51** Listen again. Complete the conversation.

A: What's the problem?

B: I've never used this GPS before and I'm having trouble getting a signal.

A: If it's raining, [1] .... Let me try … There, I think I've got it. And then [2] ...., press the button with a star. [3] .... if you want a closer view.

B: OK. Great.

A: What are you looking for exactly?

B: The helicopter pilot left a message earlier. He wants to know where to pick us up. I think the nearest place is here.

A: Hmm. It's about two days away.

B: Yes, but if he flies closer to us, [4] .... There are too many trees.

A: What about here? It looks flat. [5] ...., we might get there by the evening.

B: Maybe, [6] .... If it isn't, then [7] .... … Oh! What happened? It's gone!

A: The battery needs recharging.

Grammar zero and first conditional

4 Look at Exercise 3. Underline examples of the zero conditional and the first conditional.

5 Choose the correct options to complete the sentences.

1 If it *rains / will rain* tomorrow, we'll stay at home.
2 *I'm / I'll be* amazed if they find a solution to the problem of energy.
3 If you *connect / will connect* to the internet, I'll call you online.
4 If the helicopter arrives tonight, *we leave / we'll leave*.
5 *He usually texts / He'll usually text* when he's on his way home.
6 If you *don't / won't* type the correct password, it won't let you log in.
7 Your bank card won't work if you *don't / won't* have enough money in your account.
8 If we both see Jennifer, *do / will* you tell her our news or shall I?

6 Grammar extra *if, when* or *unless*

> ▶ **IF, WHEN or UNLESS**
>
> When you talk about things that are generally true (zero conditional), you can use *if* or *when*. There is no difference:
> *If it's sunny, we like going to the beach.* = **When** *it's sunny, we like going to the beach.*
>
> When you talk about situations in the future (first conditional), there is a difference:
> *If I see Fabio, I'll tell him. (It's possible that I will see him.)*
> **When** *I see Fabio, I'll tell him. (I am definitely going to see him.)*
>
> We use *unless* when we mean *if … not*:
> *You tell Fabio the news* **unless** *I see him before you.*
> *= You tell Fabio the news if I* **don't** *see him before you.*

a Look at the grammar box. Which pairs of sentences (1–6) have the same meaning? Write ✓ or ✗ in the box.

1 ☐

If Kate phones this evening, she'll leave a message for me.
When Kate phones this evening, she'll leave a message for me.

2 ☐

If there's space in the bags, I'll take my hair dryer as well.
When there's space in the bags, I take my hair dryer as well.

3 ☐

You won't discover the answer if you don't make a few mistakes in the process.
You won't discover the answer unless you make a few mistakes in the process.

4 ☐

We'll go without you if you don't hurry up.
We'll go without you unless you hurry up.

5 ☐

Let's go this way unless he says he has a better idea.
Let's go this way if he says he has a better idea.

6 ☐

When you don't know the answer to a question, ask your teacher.
Unless you know the answer to a question, ask your teacher.

b Complete the phone message with *when, if* or *unless*.

> Thank you for calling your bank. [1] _____ you would like to hear your account details, you need to press one. [2] _____ you would like to apply for a credit card, you need to press two. Otherwise, stay on the line and we will be happy to help you [3] _____ one of our customer service representatives becomes available. Please note that we are currently receiving a high number of calls so [4] _____ your call is urgent, we recommend you try again later. Note that we answer calls between eight in the morning and eight in the evening [5] _____ it's a public holiday.

7 Vocabulary extra items for an expedition

Make six sentences with *If we don't take …, we can't …* and these words and phrases.

~~a camera~~	satnav	an umbrella	a torch
matches	a cooker	find our location	
stay dry	make a hot meal	~~take photos~~	
light a fire	see in the dark		

1 *If we don't take a camera, we can't take photos.*
2 _____
3 _____
4 _____
5 _____
6 _____

8b Experiments and inventions

1 Vocabulary extra experiments and inventions

Complete the table with the different forms of the words.

Verb	Noun
invent	1 ....
2	communication
experiment	3 ....
4	solution
instruct	5 ....
6	decision

2 Pronunciation word stress

🎵 **52** Listen to the words in Exercise 1. Underline the main stress and write the number of syllables. Then listen again and repeat.

Example:
in<u>ve</u>nt (2), in<u>ve</u>ntion (3)

3 Complete the sentences with these verbs.

do   find   follow   get   have   invent
make   solve

1   Great inventors .... new ideas all the time.
2   We still haven't been able to .... this problem. We don't know what the answer is.
3   When you buy something with electronics inside, you should always .... the instructions carefully.
4   Scientists have to .... lots of experiments before they can reach a conclusion.
5   Did you .... the solution to the problem?
6   During the day I work in an office, but in my spare time I like to .... things. At the moment, I'm working on a new type of car!
7   We need to .... a final decision and then tell everyone.
8   The advantage with robots is that they don't .... tired.

Reading the seatbelt

4   Read the article on page 63. Which sentence (a–c) is true for the author?

a   The author thinks we need more inventors.
b   The author thinks Bohlin's invention is very important.
c   The author wants more people to use Bohlin's invention.

5   Read the article again. Answer these questions.

1   Who was Nils Bohlin?

2   When did he invent the seatbelt?

3   Who did he work for?

4   At first, did all drivers use the seatbelt in their cars?

5   Why did more and more drivers eventually use the seatbelt?

An **invention** which has **saved** millions of **lives**

In recent history, there have been some amazing inventions which have changed our lives. The aeroplane has made international travel faster and easier. The computer can store the contents of a library. And you probably know the names of some famous inventors like Henry Ford or Steve Jobs. But for every famous invention and inventor, there are many everyday objects which we don't notice and we don't know who invented them.

Take the inventor who invented the modern-day car seatbelt. Nils Bohlin's invention has saved millions of lives. Fifty years ago, Bohlin was an engineer who worked for the car manufacturer Volvo. There were other types of seatbelts, but he developed the first one which went across the chest and across the legs and then joined at the same place. Amazingly, this was an idea which no one had tried before. But it was very simple – and that's probably true of so many great inventions.

Volvo soon started selling the new seatbelt in the countries where it had the most customers. Fifty years ago, and probably still today, the biggest market was the USA. However, it took a long time for the invention to become popular there. Even in cars which had the invention, many drivers didn't use it. People enjoyed driving without a seatbelt. It was difficult to change their habits, even though more people survived a car crash when they wore Bohlin's seatbelt. Over the years, more and more governments made laws that forced drivers to wear the seatbelt, and today Nils Bohlin's simple invention still saves thousands of lives every year.

Grammar defining relative clauses

6 Underline eight defining relative clauses in the article.

7 Match the beginnings of the sentences (1–5) with the endings (a–e).

1 That's the scientist
2 She only invents things
3 I saw him speak at a conference
4 It's a device
5 That's the inventor who

a where scientists presented new ideas.
b who created the internet.
c that sends secure messages.
d invented the USB port on the side of laptops.
e which help other people.

8 Complete the article with *who, which* or *where* and these phrases.

> there is less sunlight
> the sun shines brightly
> changes with the sun
> invented the windows
> works in a hot office

Innovation news
New 'Smart Windows' control the sun

There is a new type of window [1] .... The windows go darker on the parts of buildings [2] .... This will be very useful for anyone [3] .... ! But the windows also go transparent on buildings [4] ...., and this will save on lighting bills. The two Koreans [5] .... say the windows are not expensive and last longer than other types of windows.

8c Biometrics

1 Vocabulary extra biometric technology

You are going to listen to a short lecture on the technology of 'biometrics'. First, match the words (1–8) with the definitions (a–h).

1 appearance   5 identity
2 behaviour   6 fingerprint
3 individual   7 effective
4 security   8 recognize

a the way someone does things
b the way someone looks
c the mark that your finger leaves
d special and different for each person
e safety
f who you are and what your name is
g see and know who someone is
h very good at what it does

Listening a lecture on biometrics

2 ◎ 53 Listen to the lecture. Number the topics (a–e) in the order the lecturer talks about them.

a how airports use biometrics
b a definition of biometrics
c the use of biometric technology in security
d the problems of biometrics
e how all humans are different in appearance and behaviour

3 ◎ 53 Listen again and make notes about biometric technology under each heading.

The science of biometrics
Examples of physical appearance:
1 ....

Examples of behaviour: 2 ....

Uses of biometrics
Main use: 3 ....
Problems it solves: 4 ....
Parts of the body which the technology can check:
5 ....

Problems with the technology
First problem: 6 ....
Second problem: 7 ....

Prediction for biometric technology
The technology will get 8 ....

Word focus *check*

4 Read these sentences with *check*. Match the words in bold with the meanings (a–f).

1 This technology **checks** your identity using biometrics.
2 When you arrive at the airport, you need to **check in** and get your boarding card.
3 Make sure you **check** your writing before you give the teacher your homework.
4 What time do we have to **check out** of the hotel in the morning?
5 There are **security checks** at the airport, so arrive three hours before your flight.
6 I'm **checking for** any mistakes in my job application form before I send it.

a pay and leave
b give your details when you arrive
c look carefully at something
d find out
e look for
f when officials look in your bags

5 Choose the correct option in these sentences.

1 Let's go to hotel reception first and *check in / check on*.
2 At passport control, the person *checks / checks for* your passport and visa.
3 The *security check / check-in desk* took a long time because they searched all our bags.
4 I need to *check out / check in* and pay my hotel bill.
5 Do you want me to read this and *check for / check on* any spelling mistakes?

8d Gadgets

Vocabulary instructions

1 Complete the sentences with these words.

the button	backwards	forwards
red button	the battery	

1 Turn it on with _____ at the back.
2 Pull the lever _____ for reverse.
3 Charge _____ overnight so it's ready in the morning.
4 Press the _____ to stop it.
5 Push the lever _____ to move.

Real life finding out how something works

2 💿 **54** Listen to two conversations about how two different items of technology work. Which conversation is about a helmetcam? Which is about GPS?

Conversation 1: _____

Conversation 2: _____

> **Glossary**
> **switch** (vb) /swɪtʃ/
> switch something on / off = turn something on / off

3 Put the words in the correct order to make questions.

a this / for / what / is / ?
  What is this for?
b why / you / need / that / to / do / do / ?
  _____ ?
c how / it / do / you / switch / off / ?
  _____ ?
d how / last / the / long / does / battery / ?
  _____ ?
e you / do / how / did / that / ?
  _____ ?
f does / work / it / how / ?
  _____ ?
g it / switch / on / I / where / do / ?
  _____ ?
h what / if / I / other / button / press / this / happens / ?
  _____
  _____ ?

4 💿 **54** Complete the two conversations from Exercise 2 with the questions in Exercise 3. Then listen again and check your answers.

Conversation one
A: [1] _____ ?
B: It's for filming things when you are climbing.
A: Really? [2] _____ ?
B: Well, you put the small round camera on your helmet. Then this bit goes on your belt.
A: [3] _____ ?
B: You press the red button.
A: Oh I see. Hey! That's very cool.
B: Yes, it's really easy to use.
A: [4] _____ ?
B: I'm not sure, but quite a few hours. So you can take it with you up a mountain, for example. Then when you get home you just plug it straight into the TV.

Conversation two
A: I can't make this work.
B: Let me have a look … Here you go.
A: [5] _____ ?
B: I pressed the red button.
A: Oh. [6] _____ ?
B: It moves the map around. Look. And I can press this as well.
A: [7] _____ ?
B: It shows your location and the place you want to go to.
A: I see. Oh one more thing.
  [8] _____ ?
B: Hold the red button down for five seconds.

5 Pronunciation linking

💿 **55** Listen to these sentences. Mark the links between words ending with a consonant sound and words starting with a vowel sound.

1 How does‿it work?
2 This bit goes on your belt.
3 You can take it.
4 Let me have a look.
5 I can press this as well.

6 Listen and respond responding to questions and instructions

💿 **56** Listen to someone asking questions and giving instructions. Respond using the words in the box. Then compare your response each time with the model answer that follows.

Really? How does it work?	That's very cool.
Let me have a look.	I see.

8e Arguments for technology

Writing a paragraph

1 Look at the sentences in two different paragraphs. Number the sentences (a–f and g–k) in the correct order.

Paragraph 1

   a There are many arguments for and against it.

   b CCTV is a type of technology used for security.

   c On the other hand, there is CCTV in our streets and not everyone wants to be filmed.

   d On the one hand, people can protect their houses or businesses.

   e Furthermore, it helps the police catch people.

   f Especially if they are not breaking the law!

Paragraph 2

   g For example, you can make calls from wherever you are.

   h Secondly, you can send text messages, which are cheaper, and also check your emails.

   i Finally, mobile phones also give you access to the internet.

   j In other words, modern mobile phones do much more than the traditional phone.

   k Mobile phones have totally changed the way we communicate.

2 Writing skill connecting words

Complete the paragraph with these words.

As	Finally	Firstly	For	In addition	In

Email has changed the way we write to each other.
[1] _____ , an email is easier and quicker to send than a letter. [2] _____ example, with a letter you need to go to a post box, but an email goes at the click of a button. [3] _____ , emails are usually shorter than letters and are more like conversations. [4] _____ other words, you can discuss something or solve a problem with emails.
[5] _____ , with emails you can also attach things such as large documents, photos and video, which is much more convenient. [6] _____ a result, the world sends far more emails every day than letters.

3 Match the connecting words and phrases (1–7) with the uses (a–g).

1	On the other hand	a	list something at the beginning
2	For example	b	list the next thing
3	In other words	c	contrast information
4	Secondly	d	add extra information
5	In addition	e	introduce an example
6	Firstly	f	introduce a result
7	As a result	g	say the same thing in a different way

4 Use the student's notes below to complete the paragraph.

The internet
very fast (information in seconds)
find any kind of information using a search engine
helps us with everyday information, information for work and studies

The internet has totally changed the way we find and use information. Firstly, …

_____

_____

_____

_____

_____

_____

Wordbuilding dependent prepositions

1 Match the beginnings of the sentences (1–8) with the endings (a–h).

1 I have a problem
2 Are you good
3 They're really interested
4 I depend
5 What are you working
6 I can't think
7 My house is similar
8 Do you have any idea

a at fixing things?
b on at the moment?
c on my laptop for everything!
d to yours.
e of the price?
f with my computer.
g in learning about technology.
h of a solution.

2 The sentences in each pair (1–5) use the same word with a different preposition. Choose the correct preposition to complete each sentence in the pair.

1 *about / of*
  a What do you **think** _about_ using cameras in public places? Is it right?
  b When I **think** _of_ France, I always imagine fresh bread and cheese.

2 *with / about*
  a Are you **annoyed** _____ something?
  b Why is the teacher so **annoyed** _____ us?

3 *with / at*
  a You should be a teacher. You are so **good** _____ children.
  b My brother is very **good** _____ playing tennis.

4 *to / about*
  a Would you like to **talk** _____ your problem?
  b Can you **talk** _____ Sarah? She looks lonely.

5 *of / with*
  a What's the **problem** _____ this satnav? It isn't working.
  b It's a **problem** _____ communication. No one understands him.

3 Write the words with dependent prepositions from Exercises 1 and 2 in the correct list.
verb + preposition: *think of,*
adjective + preposition: *good at,*
noun + preposition: *problem with,*

Learning skills using resources effectively

4 It's important to use different resources when you learn English. Look at these different types of resources and circle how often you use them. Think about the ones you don't often use or never use. How could you start using these resources more effectively?

How often do you ...

• use the reference material at the back of the Student's Book?	1 2 3 4
• watch the Student's Book videos more than once?	1 2 3 4
• listen to the CDs again at home as well as in class?	1 2 3 4
• ask your teacher when you don't understand something?	1 2 3 4
• ask your classmates when you don't understand something?	1 2 3 4
• practise speaking English with your friends outside of class?	1 2 3 4
• use a good dictionary to find information about words?	1 2 3 4
• search the internet to read and listen to the news in English?	1 2 3 4

1 = all the time
2 = often
3 = not often
4 = never

5 What other resources do you use to learn English? Tell your class about these resources in the next lesson and find out what other students use.

Check!

6 Do the quiz. You can find the answers in Unit 8 of the Student's Book.

1 What is a type of science which studies the design of animals? _____

2 What is an invention which you can use as an alternative to a zip on clothing? _____

3 What is the type of lighting which is more effective than normal lighting? _____

4 What is the name of the robot which is now helping NASA astronauts? _____

5 Who is the inventor that invented special glasses which don't need an optician? _____

6 What is the gadget that uses satellites and can tell you where you are? _____

9a Holiday experiences

Reading a holiday story

1 Read the story about a holiday. Answer the questions.

1 Why had the woman chosen the cottage?

2 Why did the journey take longer than expected?

3 Why did it look like someone was living in the cottage?

4 Why did she wake up on the first night?

5 What was in her daughter's bedroom wardrobe?

6 What was strange when they returned from a day at the beach?

7 Who was staying across the field from them?

8 Why was the woman surprised?

Listening details of the story

2 🎵 **57** Listen to the woman in the story from Exercise 1 telling her friend about the holiday. The details she gives are different to the story. Underline the details in the story that are different.

Vocabulary holiday collocations

3 Match the sentence beginnings (1–6) with the endings (a–f).

1 I plan to go
2 I'd like to book
3 What time do we need to check in
4 Do you want to stay
5 I need to unpack
6 In the USA it's normal to give the waiter

a a tip for 20% of the bill.
b my holiday online but the website isn't working.
c my bags first.
d at the hotel reception?
e abroad next year for my holidays.
f at a hotel or in an apartment?

Holiday Horror Stories

Home | About | Contact

Send us your favourite holiday stories and win £100 prize money for the best!

It had looked great in the brochure. It's true that there hadn't been pictures of the cottage, but there were photographs of the sea, empty beaches next to the cottage for the children to play on, and nice long walks in the nearby forest with the dog.

We arrived late at night after a six-hour drive. It's normally three hours from London, but there had been a delay on the motorway. The address on the booking form said 'Green Tree Cottage' on the Old Farm Road. In fact, we had to drive across a field to reach the place. Inside, the cottage wasn't very clean. In fact, it was full of furniture, books, pictures and objects in boxes. It was like someone else lived here.

Anyway, it was late and we went to bed. I woke up once because I thought I heard someone in the house. In the morning, my daughter said there were clothes in her wardrobe. She was right. It was full of clothes. We emptied the wardrobe and put the clothes in a box.

Later that day we had been to the beach (which wasn't next to the house but about two miles away) and when we got back the clothes were back in the wardrobe. My daughter's clothes were in the box on top of the wardrobe. I wanted to leave but my husband thought there was a simple explanation.

In the evening, as it got darker, I noticed a light at the end of the field. We walked across with the dog and we saw a small shed among the trees. We knocked on the door and a man appeared. He was the owner of the holiday cottage and lived in his shed when visitors stayed. He also asked us not to move his clothes because he needed to use the house from time to time. I couldn't believe it! The next day, we loaded the car and left.

4 Match the verbs (1–6) with the nouns (a–f) to form holiday collocations.

1 book
2 stay at
3 rent
4 buy
5 go
6 visit

a comfortable hotels
b a tour
c tickets
d sightseeing
e a bicycle
f the pyramids

5 Complete the adverts with the collocations from Exercise 4.

Take the stress out of your next holiday and
¹ _____ of Egypt with
Egyptian Adventures Travel Company. During the
day, you'll ² _____ and some
of Egypt's other historical sites. At night, you'll
³ _____ and try our country's
famous dishes.

For an alternative way to see Amsterdam, why not
⁴ _____ for a day. It's the fastest
way to ⁵ _____ and the cheapest
form of transport. Visit our website now! You can also
⁶ _____ in advance and get
a 20% discount on Amsterdam's main museums and
galleries.

Grammar past perfect simple

6 Complete this holiday story with the past perfect simple form of the verbs.

Before I visited northern Norway,
I ¹ _____ (be) to many parts of the world,
including the southernmost point of Patagonia.
I ² _____ (see) many natural wonders, but I
³ _____ (not imagine) that a place so near my
own home country of Ireland would be so beautiful.
We ⁴ _____ (drive) all day up the coast of
Norway and finally we ⁵ _____ (arrive) just as
the sun was disappearing. Above us were the Northern
Lights in the sky. The colours were amazing and they
seemed to dance. We ⁶ _____ (not expect) that
they would be so stunning.

7 Choose the correct form (past simple or past perfect simple) to complete the conversations.

Conversation 1
A: ¹ *Did you ever go / Had you ever been* to the Atlas
Mountains before?
B: No. I went to Morocco in 1999, but only to the
cities. There ² *wasn't / hadn't been* time on that
trip to travel to the mountains as well.

Conversation 2
A: I didn't know that Sandy ³ *left / had left* his job!
When ⁴ *did that happen / had that happened*?
B: Months ago. ⁵ *He wanted / He'd wanted* to leave
for ages and travel abroad. ⁶ *I received / I'd
received* a postcard from him yesterday from
New Zealand.

Conversation 3
A: Why are Josie and Bryony back from their
European tour already?
B: Well, by the time they reached Paris, the car
⁷ *broke / had broken* down three times, so they
⁸ *gave / had given* up.

Pronunciation 'd and n't

8 Read the sentences and replace words with the contractions 'd or n't where possible. In some sentences no changes are possible.

      'd
1 We ~~had~~ had a great day out with our friends.
2 We had to leave early because of the train times.
3 The hotel did not have our reservation.
4 They had not eaten since they left home in
the morning.
5 I had lost my wallet so I called the police.
6 You had left a message on my phone but you
had not said where you were.

9 🔊 **58** Now listen and check your answers. Then listen again and repeat.

9b Visiting different places

Reading talking about places

1 Read parts of postcards from five different tourists. Match the postcards (1–5) with the places they talk about (a–f). There is one extra place.

Postcard 1   a   a range of mountains
Postcard 2   b   a desert
Postcard 3   c   an island
Postcard 4   d   a historical city
Postcard 5   e   a famous statue
              f   an arts festival

2 Match the statements (a–h) with the postcards (1–5) in Exercise 1. One of the statements matches two postcards.
  a One thing was particularly special for this person.
  b You can see places which are over three hundred years old.
  c This person travelled with a group.
  d This journey involved travelling by boat.
  e This person didn't have to take a tent.
  f No cars are allowed in one area.
  g This person travelled with one other person.
  h This person had seen it but never visited it before.

1

We sailed across to this place and spent a few days here. There was no one else, so the pair of us had it to ourselves. Amazing that places still exist where there are no humans and you can just see empty beaches in each direction!

2

You'll recognize the place on the postcard, but nothing prepares you for actually seeing it with your own eyes! It's so impressive when you sail across the harbour and there it is, standing high up and looking across New York.

3

Arrived here two weeks ago. One more week to go. Have seen some great theatre and lots of great live music. I'm exhausted, but there's more to do before we go home. I think the most memorable event was a group of dancers from China. Will tell you more next week. Don't work too hard!

4

You'd love it here. There are beautiful rivers with lots of fish jumping. Our guide told everyone that bears live up here, but we haven't seen any. It's so quiet and not too many people. But don't worry about accommodation – there are always small hostels or cabins where you can stay after a long day's walking or climbing.

5

When you first arrive it all looks very modern and there are cars everywhere. But in the centre it's all pedestrianized so it's easy to walk around and admire the architecture. Lots of it was built in the seventeenth century and they've really taken care of it.

Dictation describing a holiday

3 🔊 **59** Listen to someone describing part of their holiday in Morocco. Complete the text with the words you hear.

I had an ¹ .... a tour group in Morocco. On the first day, our tour guide showed us round the centre of Marrakesh. First, we went to the square in ² .... the city called the Jemaa El Fna. It's ³ .... where people sell things, old men play musical instruments and there are people with snakes! Actually we ⁴ .... the snakes and moved away when we saw them come towards us on the ground. After a day walking round the city, everyone ⁵ .... so we relaxed at the hotel and ate great food.

The next day ⁶ .... we went by bus up the Atlas Mountains. The views were incredible as we went up, although the bus driver drove too fast for me. I ⁷ .... some of the high roads, but we safely reached the top and then the road went down to a region of green fields. We finally arrived at a small hotel and I ⁸ .... it looked ugly on the outside. But after we walked through a large gate, the owners met us with a smile and showed us round their beautiful hotel with its huge swimming pool and orange trees.

4 Pronunciation syllables and word stress

🔊 **60** Look at the words in the box. Listen to three forms of each word (e.g. *amaze, amazing, amazed*) and write the forms in the correct column of the table, according to their stress pattern.

amaze fascinate interest frighten worry
tire excite surprise

●	●●	●●
	amaze *amazed*	

●●●	●●●	●●●●
amazing		

Grammar subject questions and other questions

5 Read the description of the holiday in Morocco again. Then complete these questions with *who, what, where, why,* and a verb and an auxiliary verb where necessary.

1 ___*Who showed*___ them round the centre of Marrakesh?
2 .... they go first?
3 .... musical instruments in the square?
4 .... towards the tour group on the ground?
5 .... they relax and eat great food?
6 How .... up the Atlas Mountains?
7 .... too fast?
8 .... the tour group when they arrived at the hotel?

6 Match the questions in Exercise 5 with the answers (a–h). Then check your answers in the description in Exercise 3.

a by bus
b at the hotel
c the owners
d the tour guide
e old men
f the bus driver
g the square in the middle of the city
h snakes

7 Which questions in Exercise 5 are subject questions (S)? Which are not subject questions (O)?

1 ___*S*___   5 ....
2 ....   6 ....
3 ....   7 ....
4 ....   8 ....

9c Travel advice

Listening tipping around the world

1 🔊 **61** Listen to a radio programme about travel and holidays. Answer the questions. Choose the correct option (a–c).

1 Why do listeners write to the programme?
   a To give opinions.
   b To get advice.
   c To complain about holiday trips.

2 Who does Stella tip?
   a People who affect her holiday in a positive way.
   b Anyone who provides service.
   c No one.

3 Why are most people surprised in North America?
   a It's expensive.
   b The service is bad.
   c The tips are high.

4 What does Stella say about tipping in different countries?
   a You will pay different percentages.
   b Always pay the same amount.
   c Try to avoid tipping because of service charges.

5 Why are service charges more common?
   a Because restaurants want to charge more.
   b Because many waiters come from different countries.
   c Because it solves a problem when you have international guests.

2 🔊 **61** Listen again and make notes about the different amounts for tipping in each country.

The USA or Canada	
Central and South America	
Europe	
China or Japan	
India and internationally	

3 Vocabulary extra places in a city

Complete the words for places in a city.

1 In the summer, they have a large outdoor c__ __ __ __a in our park with some great films.
2 This m __ __ __ __m has objects from hundreds of years of the city's history.
3 The ancient c__ __ __ __ __ __ __s are right below us. People used to bury the dead there.
4 There's an exhibition of Picasso on this month at the art g__ __ __ __ __y. Let's go there.
5 This t__ __ __ __ __e is famous for its performances of Shakespeare's plays, and lots of well-known actors perform here.
6 Trains used to pass through these t__ __ __ __ls, but now they aren't used.

4 Word focus place

Read what the tour guide says on a tour of the city of London. Complete his words with the correct phrase.

a good place	all over the place
no place for	take place

So, over there is the city's biggest park. At this time of year, lots of different events ¹ _____ here in the evenings. On the left you can see the Ritz hotel, where celebrities stay. And that small restaurant next to the hotel is ² _____ to eat. Don't worry, it isn't as expensive as the hotel! As we drive down this road, there's a theatre. This part of London has theatres ³ _____ . If you want tickets, you usually need to book them in advance. Now we're passing the London Dungeon. It's fun, but it's ⁴ _____ anyone who is scared of the dark …

9d Tourist information

Listening tourist information

1 🔊 **62** A tourist is at the tourist information office on the map. He is asking for information about different places in the town. Listen to the conversation and circle the four places they talk about.

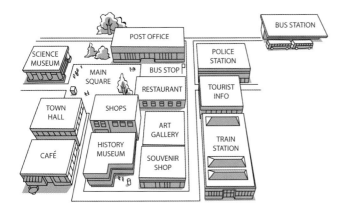

Real life requesting and suggesting

2 Complete the conversation at the tourist information office with these phrases.

Could you tell	I'm interested in	How much
Are there any	What time does	How about
You can also take	Is there any	Do you know
Another option is		

TO: Hello? Can I help you?

T: ¹_____ visiting the history museum. ²_____ the opening times?

TO: Sure. Let me check. Today is Monday, so I'm afraid it's closed all day. But it's open from Tuesday to Sunday. So it's open tomorrow.

T: Great. ³_____ it open?

TO: At nine-thirty, and it closes at five-thirty.

T: Oh right. ⁴_____ me the price?

TO: It's free.

T: That's good. ⁵_____ other museums which are open today?

TO: We have a science museum, but that's closed as well today. ⁶_____ going to the art gallery across the road?

T: I'm not sure. ⁷_____ is that?

TO: It's free for the general exhibition and five euros for the special exhibitions. ⁸_____ an interesting guided tour at midday. It's also five euros.

T: Well, OK. That might be good.

TO: You can buy the ticket for the tour at the entrance.

T: One other thing. On Wednesday I want to visit the national park outside the town. ⁹_____ public transport there?

TO: A bus leaves the bus station at ten in the morning and returns at five. ¹⁰_____ to take a taxi. It isn't too expensive.

3 🔊 **62** Listen again and check.

Listen and respond at the tourist information office

4 You want to visit the city's castle. Read the notes someone has taken, and think about how you would ask for the information. Use the phrases in the box.

The city castle
Opening times: Open every day from 10 a.m. to 6 p.m.
Ticket price: € 7.00
Take bus 15 from the station. It leaves every fifteen minutes.

I'm interested in … .
Do you know the …?
Could you tell me …?
Is there …?
How often does it …?

5 🔊 **63** Now listen to the person in the tourist information office and respond with your questions.

9e Requesting information

1 Writing skill formal expressions

Lines from two emails have been mixed up. One email is formal and one is informal. Number the lines in the correct order, starting with line a.

a | Dear Sir or Madam

b | Thanks. All the best

c | I am writing to request further information about your 'Bahamas Paradise'.

d | I would also be grateful if you would send me full prices for next summer.

e | Do you remember how much the holiday cost?

f | Yours sincerely

g | I saw your advertisement on a website but would like to receive a brochure.

h | Hi Herbert

i | Can you send me more info about that place you went to last year?

j | And what was the name of the restaurant you went to every evening?

Formal email		Informal email	
1	a	6	
2		7	
3		8	
4		9	
5		10	

Writing an email requesting information

2 Choose the correct options (a–c) to complete the letter.

---

1 _____ Mrs Waring

I am writing 2 _____ regard to your 3 _____ for more details about our package tours in the Mediterranean. I am delighted 4 _____ enclose a copy of our brochure for next year. As you will see, we are offering a greater choice of holidays than ever before.

I have to 5 _____ because I am unable to provide an up-to-date price list at this time. I hope to send this in the next two weeks. In the meantime, if you require any 6 _____ information or have questions, 7 _____ do not hesitate to contact me directly at 0700 687 5674.

Best 8 _____

H. G. Williamson
Sales department

1	a Hi	(b) Dear	c Yours
2	a with	b to	c about
3	a question	b request	c ask
4	a with	b to	c for
5	a apologize	b sorry	c afraid
6	a future	b faster	c further
7	a you	b please	c why
8	a requests	b require	c wishes

Wordbuilding *-ed* and *-ing* adjectives

1 Complete the pairs of sentences with the *-ed* or *-ing* adjective form of the words.

1 amaze
  a The view from here is ....
  b I'm .... at how much everything costs in this country.

2 fascinate
  a Tourists were .... by the pyramids.
  b The history of this region is ....

3 interest
  a Why are you so .... in this building?
  b Do you think this is an .... place to visit?

4 frighten
  a The rollercoaster is one of the largest in the world and very ....
  b Lots of people were .... by the ride at the theme park.

5 worry
  a You look ....! Don't be. The dentist is very friendly.
  b Why are you .... about your results? You always pass your exams.

6 tire
  a Everyone's .... after the long walk.
  b Carrying a heavy backpack is really ....

7 excite
  a Tonight we're going to a concert. We're really ....
  b It's always .... to visit new places and meet new people.

8 surprise
  a Was it .... to see so many friends at your party?
  b I was .... to receive a present from everyone.

Learning skills learning from your mistakes

2 How do you feel when you make a mistake in English? Which sentence (a–c) describes your opinion of making mistakes?

  a I get really angry when I make a mistake. I mustn't do it!
  b I'm scared of making mistakes.
  c Mistakes mean I am learning. I try to learn from them.

3 You can learn a lot from your common mistakes, so it's a good idea to write them on a special page in your notebook. Write the corrections in a different colour below them. Look at this page from a learner's notebook. He has written down the mistakes but needs to write all the corrections.

1 Let's ~~stay this~~ hotel.
  Let's stay at this hotel

2 I'd like to ~~rent~~ two tickets for the tour.
  ....

3 I hadn't ~~see~~ my friend for a long time.
  ....

4 Who ~~did live~~ in this house?
  ....

5 This is ~~a place good~~ to eat.
  ....

6 I'm ~~interesting~~ in the museum.
  ....

7 Could you ~~say~~ me the opening times?
  ....

4 Start a 'My common mistakes' page in your notebook. Look back through your work and write down your common mistakes.

Check!

5 Answer these quiz questions. Use information in Unit 9 of the Student's Book to help you.

1 A word meaning 'in another country' or 'overseas' (6 letters) ....

2 You give this to someone who gives you good service (3 letters) ....

3 Temples in Malta (7 letters) ....

4 Ancient places below a city (9 letters) ....

5 A type of boat in Venice (7 letters) ....

6 Some special caves in France with paintings (7 letters) ....

Unit 10 Products

10a Advertising products

Vocabulary extra advertising products

1 Match the words (1–7) with the definitions (a–g).

1 logo   5 discount
2 sales   6 customer
3 advert   7 marketing
4 poster

a the activity of selling products
b a notice (on TV, on the radio, in the newspaper, on the internet, etc.) to tell people about a product or service
c a large picture with words to advertise something
d a person who buys products
e the amount you take off the normal price
f the activity of advertising and promoting products
g a symbol to represent a company and its products or services

2 Complete these sentences with the words from Exercise 1.

1 The _____ for the sportswear company Nike is a large tick.

2 This _____ saw our advertisement and he wants to buy a bicycle.

3 There's a 10% _____ on all our cars if you buy one this week!

4 I work in the _____ department of a large company. We organize the advertising for all our products.

5 There's an _____ for a job in the newspaper today. I think you might be interested.

6 Can I speak to your _____ manager, please? I have a question about the price of this product.

7 We're having a sale this week. Can you put this _____ up in the window of the shop so people know?

Reading

3 Read the article about advertising with social media. These headings (a–d) are missing from the article. Write the headings in the article.

a How do I know if advertising on social media is effective?

b What do I post on social media?

c What kind of social media do my customers use?

d How much time should I spend on social media?

Advertise your products with social media

Nowadays, every business has to advertise its products online. Most companies have a website with pictures and information about their shop and products. And it's a good idea to sell products online as well. However, a website on its own isn't enough when it comes to online advertising. Lots of customers use social media such as Facebook and Twitter these days, so you also have to think about advertising here. Here are four questions to ask yourself about advertising with social media.

1 _____
Think about the people who buy your products, because different customers use different social media. Lots of adults use Facebook but younger teenagers are often on other social media like Instagram.

2 _____
Social media is about short messages and communicating with customers. Posting pictures and anything visual works well. Write news about what is happening at your company. Also, find out what your customers are posting and repost it.

3 _____
Don't post too often because people will get annoyed with the posts. On the other hand, don't stop posting after a few weeks. It takes time to build your social media network. Decide a regular time to work on posts.

4 _____
After all your hard work, your sales should increase. If they don't, then maybe you are using the wrong social media sites and you need to communicate with customers in other places.

4 Read the article again. According to the article, are these sentences true (T) or false (F)?

1 Most companies have a website nowadays.
2 You also have to sell your products online.
3 All customers use the same social media sites.
4 Posting photos is a good idea.
5 You should post information about your business every day.
6 Advertising using social media usually has immediate results.
7 If sales don't increase, try other social media sites.

Grammar passive

5 Complete these sentences with the present simple passive form of these verbs.

visit	make	spend	recognize	sell
advertise	transport	wear		

1 Our furniture _____ in a factory in Poland.
2 The products _____ by lorries across Europe.
3 Our clothes _____ by older people in their fifties and sixties.
4 The McDonald's logo _____ all over the world.
5 These days all our products _____ online. We don't use traditional shops anymore.
6 Most of our electronics _____ on the internet and on TV.
7 Billions of dollars _____ on advertising every year.
8 Our website _____ by about a million people every month.

6 Read these sentences about 'firsts'. Rewrite the active sentences using the past simple passive form.

1 John Pemberton made the first bottle of Coca-Cola in 1892.
The first bottle of Coca-Cola _____ .
2 Ray Tomlinson sent the first email in 1971.
The first email _____ .
3 JK Rowling wrote the first Harry Potter book in 1997.
The first Harry Potter book _____ .
4 The Wright brothers flew the first plane in 1903.
The first plane _____ .
5 Louis and Auguste Lumiere showed the first commercial film in Paris in 1895.
The first commercial film _____ .

7 Read this article. Choose the correct option.

How companies got their names

We [1] _recognize_ / are recognized the logos of these famous companies and their products and services [2] sell / are sold around the world, but where do their names come from?

- The name 'Lego' [3] makes / is made from two words in Danish: 'leg godt', which means 'play well'.
- Canon cameras [4] are called / were called 'Kwanon cameras' originally, but the company [5] changed / was changed the name to Canon in 1935 because it was more international.
- The four letters IKEA [6] take / are taken from the initials of Ingvar Kamprad, and the first letters of the places he grew up.
- The music streaming site Spotify [7] says / is said its name comes from the words 'sport' and 'identify'.
- The name for the website Amazon [8] is chosen / was chosen because it starts with the letter 'A' and comes top of an alphabetical list.

Dictation an ancient product

8 🎧 **64** Listen to a short description of papyrus. Write in the missing words.

The plant called papyrus [1] _____ _____ ancient Egyptians. It [2] _____ , _____ sandals and many other products. However, it [3] _____ writing tool in Egypt, and later it was used by the Romans. The inside of the long plant [4] _____ pieces. These [5] _____ across each other and dried. Nowadays, paper [6] _____ but [7] _____ building materials.

10b Product design

Vocabulary describing design

1 Look at the pairs of adjectives. Match each adjective with the photo (a or b) it describes.

1 up-to-date / basic

a    b

2 old fashioned / fashionable

a    b

3 out-of-date / classic

a    b

4 useful / useless

a    b

The internet of things

Nowadays we are all used to the internet in our daily lives. We use it to get information, watch videos, communicate with friends and find out the news. But some products are also designed to connect with us through the internet, and in the future, the things in our homes will do this more and more.

The basic idea behind 'the internet of things' is that it lets humans 'talk' to their devices. For example, there are fridges which can text you if you don't have any milk or if the last carton of milk in the fridge is out of date. You can also use your mobile phone to control the heating in your house via the internet. So if it's cold, you can switch the heating on when you are going home from work or school. Or if you left the heating on when you left home, you can switch it off.

In the workplace, some manufacturing companies are using the internet of things to order more tools and machines when they need them. Employers are also using the internet to check when workers are at their desk and when they aren't, which some people think is worrying. On the other hand, your computer can also tell you when you need to stand up from your desk and take a break. And more of us are wearing internet-connected devices around our wrists to check our health and measure our physical exercise.

Some people think the internet of things is bad for us because all our devices collect lots of personal data about us. Companies learn more about their customers from this. And your electronics know when you are at home and when you are out, which someone online could find out. So is there a problem for personal security? There are still lots more unanswered questions like this about the internet of things.

Reading the internet of things

2 Read the article. Answer the questions (1–8) with words and phrases from the article.

1 What are some products designed to do nowadays?

2 What is the basic idea behind the internet of things?

3 What can some fridges do if your milk is out of date?

4 Why is it useful to use the internet to connect to your heating system?

5 Why are some people worried about the way you can use the internet at work?

6 Why are some people wearing internet-connected devices around their wrists?

7 How can companies learn more about their customers?

8 What could someone online find out from the electronics in your home?

Grammar *used to*

3 Choose the correct options to complete the text.

> When I was a teenager, I didn't ¹ *use to / used to* enjoy school. I never ² *used to / didn't use to* be interested during the lessons. The teachers ³ *use to / used to* talk for hours about different subjects, but I wasn't interested. Then one day something changed. My local supermarket ⁴ *used / used to* employ people every summer, so I got a job there. For the next few weeks I ⁵ *used to work / worked* really hard and I ⁶ *used to become / became* interested in business. After the summer, I worked much harder at school. I ⁷ *used to / didn't use to* ask my maths teacher for extra homework because I wanted to be good with numbers and money. And I ⁸ *used / used to* all my spare time to read about business in the school library. Five years after I left school, I opened my first shop.

4 Complete the sentences with the correct form of *used to* and the verbs.

1 I _____ (love) fizzy drinks when I was young. I hate them now.

2 _____ (you / have) a pet when you were a child?

3 We _____ (not / take) a holiday as a family because my parents were always working.

4 My brother _____ (ride) a unicycle to work!

5 My first car _____ (never / work) properly. I soon sold it again.

6 _____ (they / know) each other when they were at college?

7 My grandmother _____ (not / let) us watch TV at her house.

8 How much _____ (you / pay) for a cinema ticket? It costs a fortune nowadays!

5 Pronunciation /juːs tuː/

🎵 **65** Listen and repeat the sentences from Exercise 4. Notice how we pronounce *used to* and *use to*.

6 Rewrite the sentences with *used to* or *didn't use to* where possible.

1 My sister wasn't interested in business when she was a student.
My sister didn't use to be interested in business when she was a student.

2 She studied music at university when she was eighteen.
not possible

3 Mark Zuckerberg started Facebook in 2004.
_____

4 My family recorded music on tape cassettes.
_____

5 Before I had a car, I cycled everywhere and I was much fitter!
_____

6 People used the first credit cards in 1920.
_____

7 My grandfather didn't pay for anything with a credit card.
_____

8 Europeans didn't eat pasta before the thirteenth century.
_____

10c Is stuff winning?

Word focus *stuff* and *thing*

1a Match the use of *stuff* in these sentences with the definitions (a–c).

1. Can you put away all this stuff on the floor, please?
2. Use this stuff to fix the broken cup.
3. I've already learnt this stuff in history lessons at school.

a. general information about a subject
b. different objects and things (which are not very important)
c. materials or substance when you do not know (or say) the exact name for it.

1b Match the use of *thing* in these sentences with the definitions (a–c).

1. This device is a thing for checking your health.
2. What's that thing on the table?
3. I'm packing all my things for the holiday into this bag.

a. an object when you do not know (or say) the exact name for it
b. an object you don't know much about, but you can explain its general purpose
c. objects that belong to a particular person

1c Which is a countable noun? Which is uncountable?

2 Complete the sentences with *stuff, thing* or *things*.

1. 'What's this _____ on your shirt?' 'I think it's orange juice.'
2. I've brought some of my old _____ from home that I want to sell.
3. This is a _____ for opening tin cans.
4. We read a lot of _____ at university which I've forgotten.
5. What's that _____ outside the house? Does it belong to you?
6. Who left all this _____ out in the kitchen?

Listening talking about stuff

3 🔊 66 Listen to six conversations about different objects. Write the number of the conversation (1–6) next to the objects they talk about (a–f).

a. TV and radio
b. bags
c. dresses
d. a phone
e. CDs
f. books, paper and pens

4 🔊 66 Listen again and choose the correct option (a–c) to complete these sentences.

1. One of the friends:
   a. offers to buy the bag.
   b. recommends a website.
   c. wants to buy a different bag.

2. The friend:
   a. doesn't have an opinion.
   b. doesn't like the dress the other person is wearing.
   c. suggests they look at another dress.

3. The father:
   a. threw all his CDs away.
   b. sold all his CDs a few years ago.
   c. isn't sure where his CDs are.

4. Jim has:
   a. left something on someone else's desk.
   b. left a few things on someone else's desk.
   c. taken some objects from someone else's desk.

5. The person is asking about the other person's:
   a. behaviour.
   b. opinion.
   c. knowledge.

6. The second speaker:
   a. agrees with the first speaker.
   b. partly agrees with the first speaker.
   c. disagrees with the first speaker.

10d Website design

Vocabulary websites

1 Read the clues (1–8) and complete the word puzzle to find the hidden word.

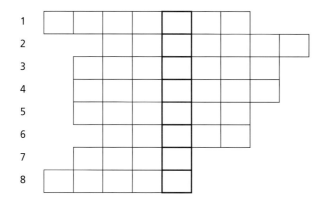

1 Every modern company needs one of these.
2 This needs to be up-to-date and interesting so that more people visit your website.
3 To communicate with the company, click here and send an email.
4 These tell you about new products and services.
5 Use this box to find information quickly.
6 Click on these to visit other sites.
7 This page is the first one you see on a website.
8 You can find information such as the company history on this page.

Real life giving your opinion

2 🎵 **67** Listen to Katarina and her manager talking about a company website. Answer the questions.

1 What does Katarina want to add to the website?

2 Why does she think customers will like it?

3 What does Katarina suggest they write about in the blog posts?

4 What does the manager suggest?

3 🎵 **67** Complete the conversation with these phrases. Then listen again and check.

> I agree   what do you think   you're right
> maybe   I see what   we could   in my opinion
> I'm not sure   we should

M: ¹ _____ about our new website Katarina?
K: It's good, but I think ² _____ add a blog.
M: That's interesting. Why do you think that?
K: Well, ³ _____ , customers like reading news on websites. So we can have news about our products.
M: ⁴ _____ , but I think that sort of thing can go on the website with advertisements.
K: ⁵ _____ about adverts, because people don't look at them. People will read about products if it's a blog post and not an advert.
M: ⁶ _____ you mean, but what would you write about?
K: ⁷ _____ we could have interviews with customers who use our products.
M: Good idea.
K: Or ⁸ _____ have photos of our employees in their free time – something fun.
M: ⁹ _____ . I suggest you write the first post and we can see if people read it.

4 Listen and respond discussing opinions

🎵 **68** Listen to someone talking to you about a new website. Respond to each sentence with an expression below and your own ideas.

> I think we should ...   Good idea!
> Maybe we could ...   I agree.

> *I think we should have a home page and then some product pages.*

> *Good idea!*

10e A review

Writing skill giving your opinion

1 Look at the sentences from different reviews. Match the beginnings of the sentences (1–8) with the endings (a–h).

1 One of my favourite
2 It's a great
3 Another good point is
4 In my opinion,
5 The only problem is that
6 On the whole, I'd
7 In general, it's
8 To sum

a place to visit in the summer.
b you can't park near the centre.
c films is *Star Wars*.
d recommend this museum to the whole family.
e that you can have lunch there.
f it's the best local restaurant.
g up, it's too expensive.
h a well-written book.

Writing a review

2 Number the parts of a review (a–g) in the correct order (1–7).

a It's a great place to eat breakfast or lunch and socialize.

b The café has quite a few good features. Firstly, the wifi is free so you can do some work on your laptop. Another good point is the atmosphere – the staff are all very friendly and always smile when you arrive.

c However, next month they plan to add more space so it will be easier to get a table.

d One of my favourite places for meeting friends is The Border café.

e One problem is that it's become too popular and so around midday it's often difficult to get a table. It's annoying when you have to wait.

f On the whole, I recommend you try The Border for the food and the fun. They also do takeaways, so if there isn't a table, you can still get a coffee and sandwich on your way to work.

g Also, one big advantage of The Border is that it's in the city centre and you can park your car round the back of the café.

3 Read these notes about an app for looking at the night sky. Then use the information to complete the review.

> Name of app? 'Starfinder'
>
> Main purpose?
> – Looking at stars at night and recognizing them
>
> Features?
> – It gives you lots of information about the star when it sees one
> – It gives you links to websites with more information
>
> Problems?
> – If you move your phone too quickly it can give the wrong information
>
> Who is it for?
> – People who are fascinated by the stars and the planets

One of my favourite apps is ―――――――――

It's a great app for ――――――――――――――

The app has quite a few different features. Firstly, it ――――――――――――――――――――――――――――

Another good point is ―――――――――――――――

The only problem with the app is ―――――――――

On the whole, it's a useful app for anyone who ――

4 Choose an app on your phone and write a review about it.

Wordbuilding word forms

1 Complete the sentences with different forms of the word in bold.

ADVERT

1 There's an _____ in the newspaper for a sale at our local supermarket.

2 _____ is a good career for creative people.

3 Do you ever _____ your products on TV?

PRODUCE

4 The new employee isn't very _____. Maybe he needs more training.

5 How much does this _____ cost?

INVENT

6 The wheel is probably the oldest _____ in history.

7 John Logie Baird was a Scottish _____ who is famous for his work with the television.

SELL

8 How many books have you _____ this morning?

9 In January lots of shops have a _____.

Pronunciation stress in different word forms

2 🔊 **69** Listen to the different forms of the root words in Exercise 1. Write the words you hear next to the correct word stress.

O: _____, _____, _____

Oo: ___advert___, _____

oO: _____, _____

Ooo: _____

oOo: _____, _____, _____

Oooo: _____

oOoo: _____

Learning skills improving your listening

3 Look at this list of ways to improve your listening. Tick (✓) the ones you use now and put an exclamation mark (!) by the ones you would like to use in the future.

1 Before I listen to something, I try to predict and write down a list of the words I might hear. So if it is a recording of a lecture, I think about the topic of the lecture and the language the speaker will need to use.	◯
2 When I like a song in English, I find the song lyrics on the internet. Then I can listen and read the words.	◯
3 I watch part of a video in English and try to understand what the people are saying. Then I watch it again with the subtitles and check my understanding.	◯
4 I listen to authentic English on the internet, for example, the news. I don't try to understand every word, but I listen for key words and numbers to understand the general meaning.	◯
5 I choose a recording which I have listened to before, from Life Pre-Intermediate Student's Book or Workbook. I listen again and I try to write down every word I hear. Then I compare my writing with the audio script in the back of the book.	◯

4 Choose one of the ideas you would like to try.

Check!

5 Look at these groups of words from Unit 10 in the Student's Book. Try to remember the connection between the words, and write a sentence with them in.

1 Hung Yen – baskets – Vietnam

2 Jawed Karim – YouTube – zoo

3 logo – upside down – Apple

4 blue – Gap – 2010

5 1986 – Walkman – English dictionary

6 The Minimalists – 2,000,000 – stuff

11a Moments in history

Listening where were you when it happened?

1 **70** Listen to five people talking about important events in the twentieth century. The speakers are all answering the question: *Where were you when it happened?* Match the speaker (1–5) with the photo of the moment (A–F). There is one extra photo.

Speaker 1

Speaker 2

Speaker 3

Speaker 4

Speaker 5

2 **70** Listen again and make notes about each speaker in the table. Try to write as much information as possible.

Speaker	The year?	Where was the speaker or the people he/she is talking about?	Any other details?
1			
2			
3			
4			
5			

A The first man on the moon

B The internet is invented

C The Second World War ends

D Nelson Mandela leaves prison

E The Berlin Wall comes down

F McDonald's opens its first restaurant in Moscow

3 Grammar extra direct speech

> ▶ DIRECT SPEECH
>
> We use direct speech to report someone's words and thoughts.
> The astronaut said, 'We've landed.'
> 'Who will follow me?' asked the President.
> She thought, 'I'm hungry.'
> Common reporting verbs include *said, asked, replied, told (someone)* and *thought.*

Write direct speech for each picture using these reporting verbs.

asked	replied	said	shouted	thought

1 The astronaut _____ .

2 The climber _____ .

3 _____ the teacher _____ to the student.

4 The customs officer _____ .

5 _____ the tourist.

4 Complete the article with these verbs.

could	loved	would	showed	was

'FIRSTS' IN SPACE HISTORY

- Yuri Gagarin was the first man in space and <u>he said he</u> ¹ _____ <u>see how beautiful the planet was</u>.
- Neil Armstrong walked on the moon in 1969 and said it ² _____ one small step for man, one giant leap for mankind.
- In 1975, astronauts from Russia and the USA met in space. One of the astronauts said that the mission ³ _____ how the two countries could work together.
- Dennis Tito paid $20,000,000 to be the first space tourist. He said that he ⁴ _____ space!
- In 2010, President Obama said the USA ⁵ _____ send the first humans to Mars by 2030.

5 Underline the reported speech in Exercise 4 and rewrite the words in direct speech.

1 *'I can see how beautiful the planet is.'*
2 _____
3 _____
4 _____
5 _____

Grammar reported speech

6 Rewrite the sentences using reported speech.

1 He said, 'I'm not interested in science.'
   He said that he _____ .

2 They said, 'We're leaving early in the morning.'
   They said that they _____ .

3 The girl shouted, 'I've found my purse!'
   The girl shouted that she _____ .

4 My grandmother said, 'I lived here when I was a girl.'
   My grandmother said that she _____ .

5 The scientist said, 'One day, we will discover the solution.'
   The scientist said that one day _____ .

6 The tourist said, 'I'm lost.'
   The tourist said that he _____ .

7 The astronauts said, 'We've landed.'
   The astronauts said that they _____ .

11b Messages from the past

Vocabulary communication

1 Choose the correct options (a–c) to complete the text.

Are you old enough to remember the days when everyone had to ^{1} _____ with each other by writing a ^{2} _____ and posting it in an envelope? Do you remember what life was like before the internet? Those were the days when information about politics and economics came printed on the morning ^{3} _____ or through radio and TV.

Now we are living in a digital age, where people write ^{4} _____ instead of letters. We no longer send holiday ^{5} _____ to family and friends but we post photos on our Facebook ^{6} _____ . And now, even writing is becoming unnecessary for communication as recording and sending a video ^{7} _____ becomes easier and easier. So is this the end of writing forever?

1	a talk	b speak	c communicate
2	a page	b letter	c advert
3	a apps	b magazine	c newspaper
4	a cards	b emails	c notes
5	a posts	b apps	c postcards
6	a page	b screen	c programme
7	a message	b presentation	c film

Reading ancient writing

2 Read the article about the Olmec stone. Match the paragraphs (1–5) with the headings (a–e).

a Other Olmec discoveries
b A new discovery
c A future hope
d The writing on the stone
e Is it real?

The Olmec stone

Archaeologists say they have discovered an ancient stone tablet in Mexico, with writing that is 3,000 years old. They have never seen writing like this before, but think that the stone tablet might come from some ancient people called the Olmec.

The stone tablet was discovered in a part of Mexico where the Olmec lived. In the past, archaeologists have found statues of huge heads made by the Olmec in the same region and you can see other Olmec objects in museums. However, none of these statues or objects have anything that looks like writing, so it's impossible to know what the writing on the Olmec stone tablet might mean.

A team of workers found the stone when they were building a road. At first they thought the tablet was just another piece of rock and nearly threw it away. Then, they noticed that it had a series of lines and symbols, so they rang their local museum. In total, there are 62 different symbols on the stone tablet in horizontal rows. The symbols show food, animals and objects such as a knife.

However, not everyone believes the writing is Olmec and some archaeologists have said the stone is a fake. For example, Christopher Pool of the University of Kentucky thinks it is strange that there are no other stones from the period with writing on. He also says that writing from a similar period is usually written vertically and not horizontally.

Nevertheless, many people are excited about the discovery and they are convinced the writing is from the Olmec. If they can find more stones like this one, then they hope to convince other archaeologists. More examples of the writing would also help them to understand the messages on the stone.

> **Glossary**
> **fake** (adj.) /feɪk/ not real or a copy
> **vertical** (adj.) /'vɜː(r)tɪk(ə)l/ down the page
> **horizontal** (adj.) /ˌhɒrɪ'zɒnt(ə)l/ across the page

3 Read the article again. Are these sentences true (T) or false (F)?

1 This is the first time archaeologists have seen this type of writing.
2 There is writing on other Olmec objects.
3 Archaeologists found the stone tablet.
4 The symbols look like everyday objects.
5 The writing goes up and down, not across the tablet.
6 Some people think they understand the message on the tablet.

Grammar reporting verbs (*say* or *tell*)

4 Complete the sentences with *say, said, tell* or *told*.

1 What did you .... ? I didn't hear you.
2 Don't .... me the answer. Let me try to guess.
3 I .... I'd be late.
4 Why did you .... her the answer?
5 Your brother .... me you were here.
6 The archaeologists .... this object was very important.
7 I .... the journalists all about what happened.
8 The students all .... they didn't understand the lesson.

5a 🔵 **71** Listen to six sentences and write the words you hear.

1 *I love this video game.*
2 ....
3 ....
4 ....
5 ....
6 ....

5b Complete the sentences to report the speech from Exercise 5a.

1 He said *that he loved that video game* .
2 She told ....
3 They said ....
4 I told ....
5 I told my manager ....
6 He told ....

6 Pronunciation contrastive stress

🔵 **72** Sometimes we stress a word to contrast it with another word. Listen to the exchanges and underline the word in B with the most stress.

1 A: I had a terrible time.
  B: But you told me you had a <u>great</u> time!
2 A: I hate carrots.
  B: But you told me you loved them!
3 A: You said you wanted to play football.
  B: No, I said I wanted to watch football.
4 A: The tickets were expensive.
  B: But you said the tickets were cheap.
5 A: Our history teacher said it happened in nineteen ninety-three.
  B: No, she told us that it happened in nineteen eighty-three.

7 🔵 **72** Listen again and repeat what B says.

11c The history of a city

Vocabulary ancient history

1 Complete the sentences with these words.

> archaeologists collectors paintings pots
> robbers soldiers statues tombs

1 Some of the _____ are three metres high and made of stone.
2 There are some new _____ in the art gallery.
3 _____ have found some ancient objects under the ground.
4 The police chased the _____ because they had stolen money from the bank.
5 These _____ were used for cooking in the past.
6 The _____ carry guns and stop people entering the area.
7 There are _____ with the bodies of kings near the pyramid.
8 Many _____ buy and sell ancient historical objects around the world.

Word focus *one*

2 Complete the sentences with the word *one*.

1 Rio de Janeiro is of Brazil's largest cities but it isn't the largest.
2 Normally the shop is busy but we've only had or two people this morning.
3 Reinhold Messner is person who has climbed Mount Everest.
4 I'd like to talk to you by one, not as a group.
5 We plan to visit Egypt day.

Listening an ancient English city

3 🎧 **73** Listen to a documentary about the English city of York. Complete the historical timeline with the information (a–e).

a Popular with tourists
b Archaeologists discover Viking objects
c The Romans start building
d The castle and cathedral are first built
e The Vikings arrive

4 🎧 **73** Listen again and complete the sentences with words and phrases from the documentary.

1 York is about _____ hours north of London by train.
2 It's halfway between London and Scotland, so _____ of tourists stop off to visit.
3 It has lots of traditional shops and _____.
4 Modern York is peaceful and relaxing, but its _____ was often violent.
5 Tourists can walk along parts of the ancient Roman _____.
6 The Vikings came from the countries we call _____ and _____ nowadays.
7 In the city museum you can see Viking objects including _____ and _____.
8 Like the Romans, William the Conqueror used York for his army _____.
9 York Minster is one of England's most important religious _____.

71 AD ➡ 9th century ➡ 11th century ➡ 1980s ➡ Now

11d My year in Vietnam

Listening my gap year in Vietnam

1 🔊 **74** Listen to a presentation by someone who spent a year after university (called a 'gap year') in Vietnam. Answer the questions.

1 What is the first part of her presentation about?

....

....

2 What is the second part about?

....

....

3 What is the third part of the presentation about?

....

....

4 What does the speaker ask for at the end?

....

....

Real life giving a short presentation

2 🔊 **74** Complete the presentation on the right with the expressions (a–l). Then listen again and check.

a I'd like to show you
b Today I would like to talk about
c Now let's move on to
d Finally, I'll talk about
e the final part of my presentation is about
f Then I'll move on to
g That's the end of my talk
h So that's everything I wanted to say about
i are there any questions
j First, I'll describe
k to sum up
l thank you for coming

3 Categorize the expressions (a–l) from Exercise 2 and complete this table.

Introducing the talk and the different parts	Ending a part of the presentation	Introducing the next part	Announcing the conclusion and ending

4 Pronunciation pausing

You are going to practise giving the presentation. Turn to the audioscript on page 122. Mark (/) in the places where you need to pause. Then practise reading the presentation aloud with the pauses.

Hello and [1] ....

[2] .... my gap year in Vietnam. [3] .... my first few days there. [4] .... my job there and I'll show you some of my photos. [5] .... my journeys through the country and describe my experiences of the culture. So let's begin by…

[6] .... the first few days. [7] .... the kind of work I was doing. We'll take a look at this photo. It shows you the school I worked in and all the children …

OK. So [8] .... my journeys. I travelled a bit at weekends, but I also took a longer journey in the last month of my gap year. So [9] .... some of my photos from that period and I'll read a few comments from my diary …

Right. [10] .... As you can see, I had an amazing few months and, [11] ...., I'd recommend it to anyone. We have about ten minutes left, so [12] .... ?

11e Requesting information

1 Writing skill correcting punctuation

Read the rules for punctuation. Then rewrite the biography about Tenzing Norgay with the correct punctuation.

> ▶ **PUNCTUATION CHECK**
> - Use a capital letter at the beginning of a sentence and with proper nouns (e.g. people, countries, nationalities, cities).
> - Use full stops at the end of sentences.
> - Use commas to separate clauses, after sequencing words at the beginning of a sentence (e.g. *firstly*, *afterwards*) and before quotation marks.
> - Use quotation or speech marks ('…') around the words spoken.

tenzing norgay is famous because with the climber edmund hillary he was the first man to reach the summit of mount everest on may 29 1953 he was born in 1914 in a village called thami near the border with Tibet he spent most of his life in the region and worked on many expeditions to everest before he reached the top afterwards his life completely changed and he travelled all over the world before he died in 1986 he said about his life it has been a long road

Writing a biography

2 Read these notes about the mountaineer Edmund Hillary. Use the notes to write a short biography about him.

Name: Edmund Hillary
Born: 1919 in Auckland, New Zealand
Died: 2008
First climb: Aged 16 in the Alps
Main climbing achievement: First man, with Tenzing Norgay, to reach the summit of Mount Everest
After Everest: Spent a lot of time raising money to help local people in the Everest region
Quote about climbing: 'It is not the mountain we conquer but ourselves.'

Wordbuilding verb + preposition

1 Replace the words in bold in the sentences (1–6) with these verbs + prepositions.

> come out   play against   think of
> talk about   pick up   work on

1   I need to **develop** a new project over the weekend. ....

2   Can you **lift** your bag off the floor and put it away? ....

3   Do you like games where you **compete with** friends? ....

4   Let's **discuss** the plans for next week. ....

5   Our new products **appear in the shops** next month. ....

6   I can't **remember** the translation for the word 'ancient'. ....

2 Match the beginnings of the sentences (1–6) with the endings (a–f).

1   I prefer to play games
2   We're talking
3   Thanks for paying
4   I spent all my money
5   Remember to take your
6   I don't agree

a   on this computer.
b   with you that gaming is bad for you.
c   with people than playing on my phone.
d   for my lunch.
e   about the homework. Do you want to join us?
f   coat with you.

Learning skills making notes

3 We often need to make notes when we listen to lectures or read textbooks. In which of these situations do you make notes?
- in meetings at work
- at college or university lectures
- in English lessons
- other situations

4 How do you write your notes? In this example, the student has started making notes on the biography about Tenzing Norgay on page 90 in this book. Notice how the student writes key words and short sentences. Do you make notes in a similar way?

> **The life of** *Tenzing Norgay*
>
> Born 1914 in Thami / Died 1986
> Summit of Everest – May 29, 1953 with Edmund Hillary
> After 1953 – travelled all over world

5 Look at the article 'The world's greatest mountaineer' on page 137 of the Student's Book. Summarize the most important information in note form.

Check!

6 How much can you remember from Unit 11 of the Student's Book? Do this quiz. Then check your ideas in the Student's Book.

1   Did Captain Scott reach the South Pole or the North Pole?
2   In which year did people first play Pong?
3   What nationality was the fisherman who found the bottle with the oldest message inside?
4   Which ancient people wanted to find out if the Mediterranean Sea and the Atlantic Ocean were connected?
5   What was the ancient name of Abu Sir al Malaq in Egypt?
6   What did Hiram Bingham discover in 1911?
7   What did Reinhold Messner climb Everest without in 1978?

12a The power of nature

Vocabulary extreme weather

1 Complete the text with these words.

> flood   snowstorm   sun   thunderstorm
> tornado   weather

We understand and can control many things in the natural world nowadays. But the ¹ _____ is one of nature's most powerful forces and it affects the daily lives of humans around the world. For example, the power of a ² _____ moving across a country can destroy homes. Heavy rain can cause a sudden ³ _____ . In colder climates, a ⁴ _____ can block the roads. But even less extreme weather can affect us both physically and also mentally. A long time outside in extremely bright ⁵ _____ can burn human skin, and changes in weather conditions can make people depressed. For example, the atmospheric pressure before a ⁶ _____ often drops and some people might suddenly feel sad or unhappy.

Listening the power of earthquakes

2 🔊 **75** The San Andreas Fault is in California. It is a place where earthquakes can begin. Listen to part of a TV programme about the fault and choose the correct options (a–c) to answer the questions.

> **Glossary**
> **fault** (n) /fɔːlt/ a crack in the earth's surface
> **geologist** (n) /dʒiˈɒlədʒɪst/ a scientist who studies the surface and rocks of the earth
> **monitor** (v) /ˈmɒnɪtə/ check, analyse
> **tremor** (n) /ˈtrɛmə/ when the ground moves because of activity in a fault

1 Where is the TV presenter talking from?
   a San Francisco
   b Near San Francisco
   c Near California

2 What does Claire study?
   a Tornadoes
   b Earthquakes
   c Hurricanes

3 What does Claire say about the San Andreas Fault?
   a That it is opening as they speak.
   b What will happen when it opens.
   c What would happen if it opened.

4 Where does the fault line go?
   a Across the USA.
   b Through the centre of San Francisco.
   c No one knows exactly.

5 Which sentence is true?
   a There has never been an earthquake in San Francisco.
   b There has never been an earthquake in San Francisco since 1906.
   c There have been earthquakes in the state since 1906.

6 What is the most difficult thing for scientists to predict about an earthquake?
   a When it will happen.
   b Where it will happen.
   c How big and how strong it will be.

San Andreas Fault

3 Dictation the San Andreas fault

🔊 **76** Listen again and complete the conversation.

Part 1

P = Presenter, C = Claire

P: So Claire, we're standing right on the fault.
   What [1] ....

   right now?
C: Well, if [2] ....
   ....
   [3] ....
   .... ,
   because the ground would be moving. But if
   we were standing in the countryside like we are
   now, [4] .... ,
   than anyone would be in a city like San Francisco.
P: Right. Because of all the buildings falling
   down.

Part 2

P: So, it is possible to guess when an earthquake
   will happen?
C: Scientists and especially geologists would
   like to be able to do that. We understand a lot
   about earthquakes and there is equipment
   which monitors them. We can predict
   where they will happen and possibly how
   big they will be. The problem is 'when'.
   We can't predict when they will happen. If
   [5] ....

Grammar second conditional

4 Choose the correct options to complete the
conversation.

A: Did you see that person who won five million
   on the lottery?
B: I know. He's so lucky. I'd never work again if I
   [1] *win / won* all that money.
A: Maybe, but you'd be bored if you [2] *didn't /
   wouldn't* go to work.
B: You're joking! First, [3] *I went / I'd go* on a cruise.
A: And then what? I think I'd still work even if I
   [4] *had / would have* lots of money. Or [5] *I set up / I'd
   set up* my own company.
B: Would you?
A: Yes, I [6] *didn't want / wouldn't want* to do nothing.
   I feel I should do something useful with
   my money.
B: Oh, I agree. [7] *I gave / I'd give* some of it to
   charity. Then I'd feel better when [8] *I spent /
   I'd spend* every day in my mansion in
   Beverley Hills.

5 Pronunciation *'d / would*

a 🔊 **77** Listen to the conversation in Exercise 4 and
check your answers. Notice the pronunciation of *'d*.

b 🔊 **78** Imagine you are person B in the
conversation in Exercise 4. Listen to person A and
respond each time.

6 Put the words in the correct order to make second
conditional sentences. Add the missing comma
where necessary.

1 If / run / I / tornado / I'd / saw / a
   If *I saw a tornado, I'd run!*

2 If / job / qualified / get / more / she'd / the /
   she / was
   If ....
   ....

3 If / go / it / stopped / 'd / raining / out / we
   If ....
   ....

4 If / had / he / a / car / bus / wouldn't / the /
   he / take
   If ....
   ....

5 If / knew / you / answer / the / they'd / tell /
   they
   If ....
   ....

12b Nature's strangest hybrids

Vocabulary places with nature

1 Read the clues and complete the crossword with places in nature.

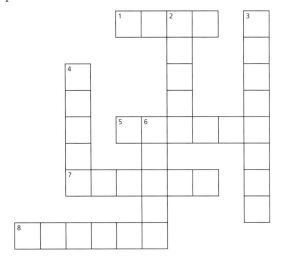

Across

1 A place to relax, often in a town or city.
5 An area with lots of trees.
7 The Sahara is one of the biggest.
8 The place next to your house with flowers and plants.

Down

2 An area of water that runs to the sea.
3 Everest is the tallest one of these.
4 You often see farm animals in one of these.
6 The area of sea between continents.

Reading interesting animals

2 Read the article about four different types of animal. Match the sentences (1–10) with the animals (A–D).

1 There are many different types.
2 People eat part of it.
3 It is compared to something which no longer lives on the earth.
4 It lives longer than many humans.
5 It's a good swimmer but a slow walker.
6 They don't all live in groups.
7 It has a face like a type of bird.
8 There are fewer of these animals nowadays than there used to be.
9 You won't see it near the coast of colder parts of the world.
10 The author thinks it is the best example of how nature makes hybrid animals.

Nature's strangest animals

Nature has produced many types of animals. Some of them are beautiful and some of them are ugly. The strangest animals are often a mixture of two different animals, called 'hybrids'. Here are four of nature's hybrids.

Ⓐ Alligator Snapping Turtle

This animal looks like something from the dinosaur age. It has the mouth of an alligator and the body of a turtle. It's even called 'the dinosaur of the turtle world.' You'll only find these strange-looking animals in the rivers and lakes of the south-eastern United States, where they can live to be 100 years old.

Ⓑ Northern Leopard Frog

The northern leopard frog used to be common in a few countries, including Canada. In particular, people in restaurants enjoyed eating the legs. However, this frog with the dark spots of a leopard is disappearing quickly. Scientists think it is probably because humans are cutting the forests down and because of air pollution.

Ⓒ Butterfly fish

You can see the butterfly fish in the warm waters of the world. There are about 114 different species and they come in many colours: blue, red, orange, or yellow. Some travel in groups and others live alone until they find a male or female partner, who they stay with for the rest of their life.

Ⓓ Platypus

When you talk about nature's strangest animals, the platypus from Australia is the winner! It has the nose and feet of a duck and its body is more like a beaver's. On land they are quite slow, but in water they are excellent swimmers and can stay underwater for long periods.

3 Look at the highlighted animal words in the article. Match the animals with these photos (1–5).

1

2

3

4

5

Grammar *anywhere, everyone, nobody, something,* etc.

4 Choose the correct option to complete the sentences.

1 There isn't *anywhere* / *anyone* in the world like home.

2 There's *someone* / *no one* who knows as much about plants as you.

3 We want to go *somewhere* / *somebody* with lots of wildlife for our holidays this year.

4 Go outside and do *somewhere* / *something* interesting instead of watching TV all the time.

5 *Everyone* / *Everything* would like to see animals in the wild but very few of us do.

6 I heard the noise of a bird but there's *nothing* / *anything* in the tree.

7 Be careful where you walk. *Everywhere* / *Nowhere* in the jungle can be dangerous.

8 Would you like *everything* / *anything* to drink?

9 *Everything* / *Something* on the earth needs water to survive.

10 There's *anybody* / *somebody* at the door. Can you answer it?

5 Complete these sentences with words from Exercise 4.

1 Hawaii is _somewhere_ that is really special because of all its natural beauty.

2 Have you had _____ to eat yet?

3 _____ in my family likes beach holidays except me.

4 Let me tell you something that _____ else knows about me.

5 Insects are _____ but you can't always see them.

6 There's _____ on TV tonight so let's go out.

7 In the Amazon rainforest, _____ you look there are trees.

8 _____ left a message for you. Can you ring them back?

12c The natural world

Vocabulary extra working with nature

1 Complete the sentences with these words.

> discovery   tool   habitat   survive
> lecture   conservation

1   This _____ is for cutting the fruit down from trees.
2   Scientists have made an important _____ about chimpanzees.
3   Lots of animals are losing their natural _____ because humans are cutting the forests down.
4   We can't _____ in the jungle without clean water.
5   Modern zoos are often involved in _____ projects to try and save different species.
6   The author is going to give a _____ about her latest book about working with lions.

Word focus *start*

2 Match the beginnings of the sentences (1–5) with the endings (a–e).

1   My mother and father started the
2   We moved here at the start
3   She started
4   They've started to
5   During the seventies a war

a   study extreme weather in science.
b   started.
c   company when they were very young.
d   working at the zoo after university.
e   of the nineteen nineties.

Listening talking about nature

3 🔊 **79** Listen to five short extracts from TV programmes. Match the extracts (1–5) with the different types of programme (a–e).

a   a news programme
b   an advertisement
c   a chat show
d   a documentary
e   a weather forecast

4 🔊 **79** Listen again. Choose the correct option (a–c) to complete these sentences.

1   The artist Georgia O'Keefe painted the 'White Place':
a   once.
b   more than once.
c   on holiday in New Mexico.

2   The weather forecaster says there will be hail:
a   in some parts of the country.
b   on higher ground where there's snow.
c   all over the country on Tuesday.

3   The man:
a   agrees with the woman.
b   disagrees with the woman.
c   gives his opinion about zoos.

4   You won't receive a special offer on tickets:
a   if you visit at the weekend.
b   if you don't have children.
c   if you don't have lunch at the zoo café.

5   When Patrick sees a tornado in the distance, he:
a   takes a photograph.
b   drives in the other direction.
c   drives as close as he can to it.

12d Discussing issues

Listening a local council meeting

1 🔊 80 Listen to three people at a local council meeting. They are discussing an area of land in the middle of the city. Answer the questions.

1 What is going to happen to the buildings and factory in the south-east of the city?

_____

_____

2 The council wants to do something with the area but what is the council's problem?

_____

3 What is the first suggestion?

_____

4 What do local people want?

_____

5 What is the second suggestion?

_____

6 What is the third suggestion?

_____

7 Why can't they use professional help to design it?

_____

8 What do they agree upon?

_____

Real life finding a solution

2 Match the beginnings of the sentences (1–8) with the endings (a–h).

1 That isn't
2 Why don't we
3 Let's summarize
4 I'm sorry, but
5 We could also have
6 No, that
7 What about
8 You might

a make it into a park or something?
b a lake there.
c we can't afford more new projects.
d be right.
e a bad idea.
f selling the land for more housing?
g what we've agreed so far.
h won't work.

3 🔊 80 Complete the conversation with the sentences from Exercise 2. Then listen again and check.

A: OK. Thank you for coming. So, as you know, we have this area in the south-east of the city with old buildings and a factory which has been closed for over ten years. It used to be an industrial area but now there are new houses in the area with people living there and a local school. So we are going to pull down all the old buildings and do something with the area.

B: It's a nice idea but the council doesn't have any money this year. ª _____ .

C: ᵇ _____ ?

B: That's a good idea.

A: Yes, but we have lots of land for housing. And anyway, I think local people want somewhere to relax.

B: I see. Well, ᶜ _____ ?

A: I agree. That's also what I was thinking.

C: ᵈ _____ .

A: How do you mean?

B: Well, when they clear away the buildings, they could dig a small lake. It would attract wildlife to the area.

A: ᵉ _____ . I like it.

B: We might suggest the idea to the local people.

C: And we could ask school children at the local school to design the park.

A: Nice idea, but I think this needs some professional help.

B: ᶠ _____ . We don't have any money to pay them. I think we need local volunteers from the community to help ...

C: Yes, ᵍ _____ .

A: So, ʰ _____ . We all agree that it's a good idea to clear the area, but not to build anything on it. We want to build a park or green space for local people to relax in.

B: And perhaps with a lake.

A: With a lake. However, we don't have much money for this, so we need to approach the local community and ask for ideas and volunteers ....

4 Listen and respond **responding to suggestions**

🔊 81 Listen and respond to four suggestions for a local park. Use some of these phrases. Compare your responses with the suggested answers.

> That's a good idea.   Yes, but ...   I'm not sure.
> Sounds great!   Maybe.   No, that won't work.

> How about building a new park for local people?

> That's a good idea.

12e A place for nature

Writing skills planning an article

1 A student has made these notes about a place called Kew Gardens. Match the notes (a–i) with the three parts of the mindmap (1–3).

a   1840

b   growing rare plants and flowers

c   for specialists who want to study and research plants

d   south-west London

e   the Pagoda, which was built in 1762

f   100 attractions, including an art gallery

g   to educate people and to keep many species of different plants alive

h   the Treetop Walkway

i   to get children interested in trees

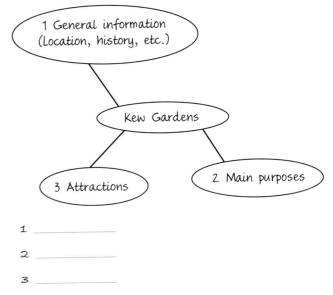

1 General information (Location, history, etc.)

Kew Gardens

3 Attractions

2 Main purposes

1 ....

2 ....

3 ....

Writing an article

2 Complete this article with information from the notes in Exercise 1.

KEW GARDENS

Since it opened to the public in ¹ ...., thousands of visitors have come to walk around Kew Gardens, which is located in ² .... It started as a place ³ .... from all over the world. Today it is a place ⁴ .... , as well as a place for the general public to enjoy nature.

When you visit Kew Gardens, you can spend all day outside if the weather is good. But don't worry if it rains because it has over ⁵ .... Some of its buildings are also very old, such as ⁶ ....

One of its most popular tourist attractions, which everyone visits, is ⁷ .... It is 200 metres long and 18 metres high, so you walk through the tops of the trees and learn about them. It's a great way ⁸ .... , but don't go up if you are scared of heights.

Overall, it's the mixture of old and new which makes Kew Gardens so popular with people. In addition, it has a very serious aim, which is ⁹ .... which are in danger of disappearing from the Earth.

Wordbuilding adjective + noun collocations

1 Read part of a weather report. Underline six pairs of words with an adjective and a noun.

> After a weekend of <u>violent</u> <u>storms</u>, the good news is that the country will return to normal. If you live in the north of the country, there will be some heavy rain through the night, but by morning this will disappear and you'll have a day of bright sunshine. You won't get any rain if you live further south, but expect some strong winds after midday. Other than that, you'll have a beautiful day.

2 Match these nouns with the groups of adjectives. Use a dictionary to help you if necessary.

> attraction   climate   news   park   rain
> ~~storm~~   sun   wind

1   fierce, freak, violent .... *storm*
2   heavy, light, pouring ....
3   strong, light, blustery ....
4   bright, hot, setting ....
5   local, national, public ....
6   popular, main, biggest ....
7   warm, cold, hot ....
8   good, bad, breaking ....

Learning skills assessing and continuing your progress

3 You are probably at the end of your course. Answer the questions on the self-assessment questionnaire. After each answer, write a comment to explain your answer.

Check!

4 Write an answer or an example for each of these items. Then check your answers in Unit 12 of the Student's Book.

1   A type of storm ....
2   The window on the front of a car ....
3   Another way of saying 'anyone' ....
4   A type of extreme weather ....
5   A sentence using the second conditional
....
6   The punctuation that separates two clauses in a sentence ....
7   An adjective which collocates with the word 'habitat' ....
8   Another way of saying 'What about going to the cinema?' starting with the words 'Why don't we …'

Self-assessment questionnaire

① **How would you describe your progress in English on this course?**

Excellent ☐   Good ☐   Satisfactory ☐   Not very good ☐

Comment on your answer: ....

② **If you take another course, which areas would you like to work on most?**

Speaking ☐   Reading ☐   Writing ☐   Listening ☐   Grammar ☐   Vocabulary ☐   Pronunciation ☐

Comment on your answer: ....

③ **If you are taking a break from your English course (perhaps you have a holiday), which of these could you do to continue improving your English?**

- read a book, magazine or newspaper in English
- use the internet in English
- use self study books and computer programs for learning English
- repeat some of the exercises in this workbook and watch the videos in the Student's Book again
- meet with friends again from your English course and practise English
- visit a country where people speak English

Any other ideas? ....

④ **What question(s) do you have for your teacher before the end of the course? Write it here and ask your teacher to reply.**

🎧 82

LISTENING TEST

SECTION 1

Questions 1 and 2

*Choose the correct letter, **A**, **B** or **C**.*

Example

Steffi will leave for Australia

A tomorrow.

(B) a week from now.

C a month from now.

---

1 What is the name of the hotel where Steffi will work?
   A Hotel Bristol
   B Hotel Carlton
   C Hotel Ambassador

2 Where in the hotel will Steffi work at first?
   A on reception
   B in the dining room
   C in the manager's office

Questions 3–10

Complete the notes below about Steffi's work placement.

*Write **NO MORE THAN TWO WORDS AND/OR A NUMBER** for each answer.*

Working hours: 30 per week

                  3 .... hours per day.

Start time: **4** .... for the first week.

Day off: **5** ....

Accommodation: Costs nothing if you stay in a **6** ....

Staff benefits: **7** .... is provided free each day.

                  Discount in the **8** ....

Name of mentor: **9** ....

Extra duty: Produce a **10** .... every week.

SECTION 2

Questions 11–13

Choose the correct letter, A, B or C.

11 The language school is located
   A near the railway station.
   B on the edge of the city.
   C next to the university campus.

12 Most students at the school stay
   A in a student residence.
   B with a local family.
   C in a shared house.

13 Students at the school have free use of
   A a football pitch.
   B tennis courts.
   C a gym.

Questions 14 and 15

*Choose **TWO** letters, **A–E**.*

Which two facilities are available in the library?

A books to borrow overnight
B unlimited internet access
C daily newspapers
D weekly magazines
E films on DVD

Questions 16–20

Complete the table below.

*Write **NO MORE THAN TWO WORDS AND/OR A NUMBER** for each answer.*

Hours per week	Price	
15 hours	£430	**16** .... only – General English **17** .... students per class
18 hours	**18** £.......	General English plus exam preparation Ten students per class Free afternoon on **19** ....
21 hours	£495	Intensive exam preparation Eight students per class Includes one **20** .... each week

SECTION 3

Questions 21 and 22

Complete the sentences below.

Write **NO MORE THAN TWO WORDS** *for each answer.*

Traffic Survey

- Adam and Becky have to do some research into road traffic in their area.

  Their work will take **21** .... weeks to complete.

- They will get advice from the local police.

  They will concentrate on the road which passes the local **22** ....

Questions 23–26

Who will do each of the following tasks?

A Adam
B Becky
C Both of them

*Write the correct letter, **A**, **B** or **C**, next to questions 23–26.*

Tasks

23 count the number of vehicles

24 interview some drivers

25 write a questionnaire

26 save the data on to a laptop

Questions 27–30

*Choose the correct letter, **A**, **B** or **C**.*

27 They agree that the main focus of the questionnaire will be to find out
    A why drivers chose to travel at a particular time.
    B why drivers decided to travel by car.
    C why drivers took that route.

28 They will include an extra question in the questionnaire on the topic of
    A other transport options.
    B car parking facilities.
    C global warming.

29 What is Becky's attitude to writing the report on the survey?
    A She'd like to do it with Adam's help.
    B She thinks Adam would do it better than her.
    C She believes they should each write a draft first.

30 Adam will present the report to the class because
    A he is a more confident presenter.
    B it will be good experience for him.
    C Becky would find it difficult to do.

SECTION 4

Questions 31–33

Complete the sentences below.

Write **NO MORE THAN THREE WORDS** *for each answer.*

Causes of falling population

Less food because **31** .... were cleaner

Killing of birds by people who believed they were **32** ....

Some people collected the bird's **33** ....

Questions 34–37

Complete the table below.

Write **NO MORE THAN THREE WORDS** *for each answer.*

Year	
1903	**34** .... for Red Kite conservation formed
1986	re-introduction programme planned
1989	birds brought to England from Sweden and **35** ....
1989	total number of **36** .... birds released
1992	first successful breeding in the wild
1996	re-introduction in **37** .... begins

Questions 38–40

Complete the notes below.

Write **NO MORE THAN THREE WORDS** *for each answer.*

Criteria for re-introduction

- The birds must have disappeared due to **38** .... actions.
- A suitable **39** .... still exists.
- The introduced birds must be **40** .... similar to those who died out.
- The removal of birds from other places must not do any harm there.

READING TEST

Questions 1–5

Look at the six advertisements for student accommodation, A–F.

For which advertisements are the following statements true?

Write the correct letter (A–F) in boxes 1–5 on your answer sheet.

NB *You may use letters more than once.*

1 It is possible to cook in the room.
2 Food is provided as part of the price.
3 You have your own bathroom.
4 The room is available for a limited period only.
5 There is a safe place to keep your bicycle.

A

ROOM AVAILABLE

- Small room available in a shared student house
- Use of kitchen, sitting room and shared bathroom
- Handy for university and city centre

Sorry no space for bicycles indoors
Small breakage deposit payable in advance
Non-smokers only

CALL 030-4132-9860

B

LARGE SINGLE ROOM AVAILABLE

- Hot and cold running water
- Use of shared bathroom
- Parking space available on request
- Internet connection (payable monthly)

Annual contract – rent payable monthly
References required

CALL 030-7658-0098

C

ARE YOU LOOKING FOR A NICE ROOM IN A CLEAN HOUSE?

- We are four post-grad students looking for a housemate
- The house is in a good suburban area close to public transport links
- The room has use of a shared kitchen and bathroom
- Meals are eaten together (mostly vegetarian) and costs shared
- Space for one bicycle in the (lockable) garden shed

Reasonable rent payable monthly in advance
All applicants will be interviewed

CALL MEL ON 030-9909-7786

D

SINGLE ROOM AVAILABLE IN A FAMILY HOUSE

- Small room with TV
- Rent includes meals on a half-board basis
- Would suit an overseas student
- Eat with the friendly family – practise your English!
- Close to bus routes (city centre 20 minutes)

Pay weekly in advance
No long-term contract involved

CALL 020-3321-0987 FOR DETAILS

E

ROOM AVAILABLE IN A STUDENT RESIDENCE

- Purpose-built block with laundry, internet access and shared kitchen
- Private shower and wc
- Ample car parking
- Supervised entrance staffed 24 hours a day

Six-month contract
Payment in advance quarterly

CALL PROPERTY MANAGEMENT ON 030-9998-9964

F

ANYBODY WANT TO USE MY ROOM FOR THE SUMMER?

I'M OFF TRAVELLING, SO THE ROOM WILL BE FREE FOR TWO MONTHS IN JULY AND AUGUST

- It's a nice room in a shared house
- Small kitchen corner with microwave and sink
- Bathroom shared with one other student (probably away too!)
- Close to the university sports ground
- City centre four miles

Come and have a look and make me an offer

GILES 030-9988-6654

Questions 6–14

Answer the questions below.

Write the correct section (A–E) in boxes 6–14 on your answer sheet.

Which section of the website (**A–E**) should you click on if:

6 you have received a letter at your house which is addressed to somebody you don't know?

7 you have a large envelope to post which is not very heavy and you want to know if it will cost more?

8 you want to send some books to a friend in another country?

9 you want to know if you are allowed to send fresh food through the post?

10 you would like to post some money to your family and want to know the best way?

11 you have to send an urgent letter and need information about the fastest service?

12 you are moving to a new address and want your mail sent there instead of to your current address?

13 you want to pay for postage over the internet?

14 you want advice on the best type of envelope to use for a small parcel?

Information for Post Office Users

A Sending UK letters and parcels
Compare sending options
First and Second Class mail
Standard Parcels
Express Parcels
Special Delivery™
Recorded Signed For™
Royal Mail Sameday®

B Receiving letters and parcels
Compare services
Redirection options
Keepsafe™ mail holding service
PO Box®
Royal Mail Local Collect™
Wrongly delivered mail

C Overseas letters and parcels
Compare overseas sending options
Surface mail
Airsure®
International Signed For™
Airmail
International Parcels

D Buy stamps online
Personalize stamps online
Stamps and collecting
Online Postage

E Mailing guide
Compare sending options
Weight and size guide
Clear addressing
Wrapping and packaging
Restricted and prohibited goods
Sending cash
Customs information
Delivery exceptions
Articles for the Blind
Overseas clear addressing

SECTION 2

You should spend about 20 minutes on Questions 15–27, which are based on the two texts below.

Questions 15–20

The text on page 108 has six sections, **A–F**.

*Choose the correct heading for sections **A–F** from the list of headings below.*

*Write the correct number **(i–viii)** in boxes 15–20 on your answer sheet.*

List of Headings

i	what to do if you have failed a driving test
ii	what to do if you want to drive something bigger than a car
iii	what to do if you have any physical problems driving
iv	what to do if you are only visiting the country for a short time
v	what to do if you are going to stay and live in the country
vi	what to do if you come from a country outside Europe
vii	what to do if you are a professional driver
viii	what to do if you want to get a UK driving licence

---

15 Section **A**

16 Section **B**

17 Section **C**

18 Section **D**

19 Section **E**

20 Section **F**

Driving in the UK
Advice to drivers from countries within the European Community and European Economic Area

Section A

If you hold a valid Community driving licence and are coming to the UK for a limited period, you can drive any vehicle if the full entitlement for that vehicle is shown on the licence.

Section B

If you are coming to live in the UK for a longer period, a valid Community licence issued on the strength of a driving test within the EC/EEA will allow you to drive in GB for a set period.

While your licence remains valid, you may drive in the UK:
- until aged 70 or for three years after becoming resident, whichever is the longer period
- until aged 45 or for five years after becoming resident, whichever is the longer period
- if you are aged over 45 (but under 65) until your 66th birthday or for five years after becoming resident, whichever is the shorter period
- if you are aged 65 or over for 12 months after becoming resident

In order to continue driving after these periods, you must get a British driving licence.

Section C

You must tell the DVLA about relevant conditions or disabilities that existed before you came to the UK and which you may have already notified to the authorities. This also includes any conditions you have recently become aware of. In most cases, the rules will be the same as those in other EC/EEA countries although there may be some differences. Higher visual standards apply for vocational drivers in this country.

Section D

If you want to take a British driving test, you must be a resident in the UK. However, if you have moved to the UK, having recently been a permanent resident in another state of the EC/EEA, you must be a resident in the UK for 185 days in the 12 months before your application for a driving test and full licence.

To take a UK driving test you will need to either:
- apply for a UK counterpart licence (D58/2) by completing a D9 enclosing your Community driving licence, or
- exchange your community licence for the British equivalent and request the appropriate provisional entitlement

A provisional licence document is issued free of charge. However, the appropriate fee must be paid and your Community licence surrendered in exchange for a UK one when claiming the full entitlement.

Section E

Community licence holders with category B entitlement can also drive certain vehicles in the UK which are exempt from the normal large vehicle driver licensing requirements. These include non-commercial minibuses driven on a voluntary basis, permit minibuses and large vehicles such as agricultural motor vehicles and road construction vehicles. Further details about these vehicles and the conditions that apply to them can be found in the fact sheet 'Special Licensing Arrangements For Drivers of Large Vehicles' available from the DVLA.

Section F

If you drive a coach or lorry as your job, you can exchange your non-UK driving licence for a UK one, but it might affect your Driver Certificate of Professional Competence (CPC). Find out what rules apply if you exchange your driving licence while you have Driver CPC or if you want to get it.

Questions 21–27

Read the text below and answer questions 21–27.

The Driving Test
A driving test in Britain is made up of a theory test and a practical test. You cannot normally take the practical test without first having passed the theory test. You pay a fee for each part of the test – for details, see under heading Fees. Before you can apply for a test, you must have a valid Great Britain or Northern Ireland provisional driving licence.

The Theory Test
The theory test is in two parts. The first is a computerized touch screen test in which you have to select the correct answer from a number of choices. The second part is called the hazard perception test. You will be shown a set of video clips of driving hazards and asked to click the mouse button as soon as you spot a hazard. You have to pass both parts of the theory test at the same sitting in order to pass.

The Practical Test
The practical test will test your ability to exercise adequate control of your vehicle and normally lasts 40 minutes. If you have a physical disability, you will be asked to demonstrate any special controls on your vehicle. The practical test also includes two questions on vehicle safety, designed to make sure that you know how to check the safety of your vehicle. Topics covered are tyres, brakes, fluids, lights, reflectors, direction indicators and horns. If you fail, or do not take the practical test within two years of having passed the theory test, you will have to pass the theory test again before you can apply for a practical test.

When you have passed the practical test, if you have a photocard provisional licence and your personal details have not changed, you can hand it over to the examiner, and a full licence will be issued to you automatically. Otherwise, you must apply to the Driver and Vehicle Licensing Agency (DVLA) for your full licence within two years of the test date. If you don't do this, you will have to take the practical test (and the theory test) again.

Probationary Period
When you pass your driving test for the first time, you will be subject to a two-year probationary period. This applies to anyone driving on a licence issued by the DVLA. The two-year period begins on the day you first pass the practical test. If during the probationary period you are convicted of driving offences for which six or more penalty points are awarded, your driving licence will be revoked. If your full driving licence is revoked, you will revert to learner status and be treated as if you never passed a driving test. To continue driving, you will have to get a provisional driving licence and drive with learner's plates until you have passed both the theory and practical parts of the driving test.

Questions 21–27

Complete the notes below.

Choose **NO MORE THAN THREE WORDS AND/OR A NUMBER** *from the text for each answer.*

Write your answers in boxes 21–27 on your answer sheet.

The Driving Test
There are two parts to the test.
You have to take the **21** .... first.

The Theory Test
In the first part, you have to answer questions on a **22** ....
In the second part, you watch some **23** .... of the problems drivers face.

The Practical Test
The test takes **24** .... to complete.
You are asked about **25** .... during the test.
If you pass the test, give your **26** .... to the examiner.

Probationary Period
This lasts for two years.
You lose your licence if you get six or more penalty points for **27** ....

SECTION 3

You should spend about 20 minutes on Questions 28–40 which are based on the text below.

THE HISTORY OF BADMINTON

Badminton is a racquet sport in which two or four players hit an object called a shuttlecock backwards and forwards across a high net. Some people regard it as the oldest racquet sport in the world, although the earliest forms of the sport probably didn't use a racquet, and the net is a relatively recent innovation.

A shuttlecock is a lightweight ball made of cork, with feathers attached to it to help it fly. It is thought that shuttlecocks were first used about 2,500 years ago in China – although they were kicked rather than being hit with a racquet in those days. A racquet sport using shuttlecocks was certainly known in ancient Greece around 2,000 years ago, as well as in China and Japan, and a version of the game has been played by children across Asia ever since. The aim was to keep hitting the shuttlecock backwards and forwards for as long as possible. The modern game we call badminton was developed in England, however, and not until the 19th century.

British soldiers learnt to play a game using shuttlecocks whilst serving in India from the middle of the 18th century onwards. When they came home, they brought the game with them. At this point, it was called Poona – named after a place in India – and from about 1860, it became popular in England. That's where a net was first introduced in 1867, and the modern system of scoring began to evolve, although there were lots of disagreements about the rules amongst the players, and no official organization to govern the sport.

All this changed in 1887. The name 'badminton' was introduced after a famous party at a country house of that name in that year. At the party, a game was played that was very similar to the one we call badminton today. A set of modern rules was drawn up and published in 1893, and the Badminton Association of England was formed in 1895 to govern the new sport and organize championships. The first of these were held in 1899 and 1900, for men and women respectively. Badminton can be played by both men and women, although slightly different rules and scoring systems apply.

The new sport soon became very popular in England. By 1920, there were 300 badminton clubs in the country, and that figure had risen to 500 by 1930. At the same time, the sport was catching on in other countries too, and in 1934 an International Badminton Federation (IBF) was set up. The IBF decided to run international championships in 1939, but because of the Second World War, the first one didn't take place until 1948, and then only for men. The first international women's championships were held in 1957.

Badminton was first played at the Olympic Games in 1972, but only as a demonstration sport – there was no actual competition and no medal winners. Although this happened again in 1988, it was 1992 before badminton was played as a fully recognized Olympic sport – with the mixed doubles being added in 1996.

Badminton is now one of the most widely played sports in the world. It is one of the fastest racquet sports, with shuttlecocks travelling at up to 260 miles per hour in top competitions, and so is very exciting to watch as well as play.

Questions 28–34

Complete the table below.

*Choose **ONE NUMBER ONLY** from the text for each answer.*

Write your answers in boxes 28–34 on your answer sheet.

YEAR	EVENT
28	The modern game was first played at Badminton House in England.
29	The first written rules for the game called badminton became available.
30	A national badminton organization was formed in England.
31	The first men's national championships were held in England.
32	An international badminton organization was formed.
33	The first international competition for women was held.
34	Badminton became an official Olympic sport.

Questions 35–40

Do the following statements agree with the information given in the text?

In boxes 35–40 on your answer sheet, write

TRUE	*if the statement agrees with the information*
FALSE	*if the statement contradicts the information*
NOT GIVEN	*if there is no information on this*

35 People in China used to kick shuttlecocks to each other.

36 The shuttlecock was invented in Greece.

37 The badminton net was first used in India.

38 Women's badminton has the same rules as men's badminton.

39 Men and women can play against each other in the Olympic Games.

40 A shuttlecock can travel faster than a tennis ball.

WRITING TEST

TASK 1

You should spend about 20 minutes on this task.

People in your area are having problems with their internet connection.
Write a letter to the company which provides the connection. In your letter
- *describe the problems*
- *explain how they are affecting people*
- *say what the company should do to help*

Write at least 150 words.

You do not need to write any addresses.

Begin your letter like this:
Dear Sir or Madam,

TASK 2

You should spend about 40 minutes on this task.

Write about this topic.

People should work a fixed number of hours per week, and employers should not ask anybody to work more than this.

Give reasons for your answer and include any relevant examples from your own knowledge or experience.

Write at least 250 words.

SPEAKING TEST

PART 1 – INTRODUCTION AND INTERVIEW

Let's talk about where you went to school.
- Describe the secondary school you went to.
- What did you like about the school?
- What didn't you like about it?
- Which subjects did you enjoy studying most? Why?

PART 2 – INDIVIDUAL LONG TURN

Candidate Task Card

> Describe a film you enjoyed watching.
> You should say:
> - which film you watched
> - why you decided to watch it
> - who you watched it with
> - why you enjoyed watching it.

You will have to talk about the topic for one to two minutes.

You will have one minute to think about what you are going to say.

You can make some notes to help you if you wish.

Rounding off questions
- Has the film had good reviews?
- How often do you go to the cinema?

PART 3 – TWO-WAY DISCUSSION

First of all, let's consider watching films.
- How expensive is it to go to the cinema in your country?
- Is going to the cinema better than watching a film at home?
- Do you think there are too many films on TV? Why (not)?

Finally, let's talk about famous film stars.
- Why do you think film stars often become celebrities?

Audioscripts

Unit 1

🔊 2

A: Hey, there's a quiz here to test your stress levels. You said you were stressed all the time, so let's find out.
B: Er, OK. I don't really have time. I have to get this report finished.
A: That's just my point. You need to take a break at lunchtimes.
B: OK, then. Ask me.
A: Do you often worry about money?
B: Er no, not really. I don't have time!
A: OK. So we'll say once a month. Two. Do you have problems sleeping? Never, sometimes or always?
B: Well, it depends. At the moment, no, but sometimes I stay awake thinking about work and things.
A: OK, so that's … sometimes. Three. Do you find it difficult to concentrate?
B: Well, at work I do because people interrupt me all the time with things like quizzes!
A: I think you're fine, so I'll tick 'rarely'. And the last one. Describe your lunchtimes. Do you do work while you're eating your lunch?
B: Always. It's the only time I do things like answer all my emails.
A: OK, I'll tick 'a'. But you know, you should leave the office and go for a walk.
B: Well, that's great in theory but …

🔊 3

a   I'm driving to the city.
b   You are not coming.
c   She's leaving now.
d   It isn't raining.
e   Why are they running?
f   We aren't stopping anywhere.

🔊 4

I usually get up at about seven o'clock and go running for half an hour. Then I feel ready for the day. I leave the house at about eight thirty and arrive at the hospital by nine. Currently, I'm seeing lots of children with flu. After work, I often walk home. Sometimes friends come round for dinner, but I need eight hours of sleep a night, so I'm always in bed by eleven o'clock.

🔊 5

I = Interviewer, D = Dunn
I: What makes you feel happy? Is it food that tastes delicious? A painting that looks beautiful? Or maybe just going to a café and having a coffee with friends. To tell us what makes us happy, I'm talking to psychologist Elizabeth Dunn. So Elizabeth, I know that you do a lot of research into happiness and in particular into money and happiness. So tell us, how much money do you need to make you happy?
D: It's a complicated question. Some people think money is the most important thing in the world for happiness. That's definitely not true. Some people think that money doesn't make you feel happier. That's also not true.
I: So, perhaps the question isn't about money but how people spend it.
D: Yes, to find out we did an experiment with some students. We gave them twenty dollars in the morning, and one group spent it on themselves and the other group spent it on someone else. By the end of the day, the people who spent it on others were happier.

I: So, we need to think about the way we use money.
D: Yes, this is something a lot of people find. Often it's the experiences that you have. Like visiting a new country or going to a concert to listen to your favourite musician.

🔊 7

D = Doctor, P = Patient
D: How do you feel today?
P: Not very well. I've got a terrible sore throat.
D: I see. Let me have a look. Open wide. Yes, it's very red in there.
P: I've also got a bad cough.
D: Do you feel sick at all?
P: No, not really.
D: Have you got a temperature?
P: I don't think so. I don't feel hot.
D: Let me check it … Yes, it's a bit high. Do you have anything for it?
P: I bought some pills at the pharmacy, but they didn't do any good.
D: Well, take this prescription to the pharmacy. You need to take some different pills. They are good for your throat. Take one every four hours. You need to go to bed for a couple of days, and try drinking lots of water.
P: OK. Thanks.
D: If you still feel ill in a few days, come back and see me, but I think it's flu. Everyone has it at the moment.

🔊 8

F = Friend, MA = Model answer
F: I've got a headache.
MA: You need to take some pills.
F: I've got a sore throat.
MA: Try drinking some hot water with lemon and honey.
F: I've got a bad back.
MA: Go to bed for a couple of days.
F: I feel sick.
MA: You need to see a doctor.
F: I've got a high temperature.
MA: Take this medicine. It's good for flu.

🔊 9

P = Patient, R = Receptionist
P: Hello, I'm George Braun, I have an appointment with Doctor Swan.
R: Good morning. As it's your first time visiting Doctor Swan, we'll need some information, so can I ask you a few questions?
P: Sure. Go ahead.
R: So it's Mr G Brown. Do you have a middle initial?
P: Yes, it's P for Paul. But my surname is Braun not Brown. That's B-R-A-U-N.
R: Oh, OK. Sorry about that. And what's your date of birth?
P: The seventh of June, 1967.
R: Seventh of June, 1967. And I need your address.
P: Err, well I'm staying with a friend at the moment, so I don't have a permanent address.
R: Well, can I take your friend's address and then you can change it when you move.
P: OK, so it's 21 Carter Street. That's C-A-R-T-E-R street. The postcode is HP12 6RJ.
R: Right. Do you have a daytime number?
P: Yes, the best number is my mobile. That's 0773 946 364
R: And now I have a few questions about your health. If you don't want to answer them that's OK. Overall, how would you describe your general health. Good? Just OK? Not good?

P: Overall, it's good I think. I do quite a lot of exercise and I eat well.
R: How much exercise do you do a week – more or less?
P: I go running three times a week. So that's about three hours.
R: Good, Anything else as well as running?
P: Err, I go swimming sometimes. And I like walking at weekends with friends.
R: So running, swimming and walking. Right. I'll give you this form and can you give it to the doctor when you see him.

Unit 2

🎧 10
1 You mustn't play.
2 They don't have to win.
3 He can lose the match.
4 The team must score another goal.
5 A player can't hit the ball twice.

🎧 12
Kristi Leskinen is a famous skier. She loves skiing all over the world but her favourite place is Mammoth Mountain in the USA. She's good at other sports such as kayaking but she doesn't like running or going to the gym. Recently she was in a TV show called *The Superstars*. In the show, famous sports people compete in different sports that they don't normally do. Kristi won the competition. But soon it's winter again so she needs to go back to the mountains and start training again. This year she'd like to win a lot more medals.

🎧 13
Freediving is the general word for any type of underwater sport without any kind of breathing equipment. So you have to take a deep breath before you go underwater. One of the most competitive types of freediving is when a diver goes deep under the water. A Swedish woman called Annelie Pompe has the world record in freediving. She went down 126 metres into the Red Sea with no air.

Annelie loves being in the sea and she likes swimming without lots of equipment. She spends every weekend training in the sea, and before a competition, she trains for about twenty hours a week. However, she also has time for other sports and these help her prepare for freediving. For example, she does yoga in the morning because it helps her to relax. She also goes running, does some weightlifting and goes cycling.

Annelie also likes mountain climbing. In 2011 she climbed Mount Everest and became the first Swedish woman to climb the mountain from the north side. For Annelie, adventure is about going to the deepest and to the highest parts of the world!

🎧 14
A: Hey, this looks interesting.
B: What?
A: This leaflet for fitness classes at the gym. Are you interested in doing something like that?
B: Maybe. But I'm not very good at sport.
A: But this isn't competitive. It's for getting fit. This one sounds good. Boot Camp. What about joining that?
B: What is Boot Camp?
A: It's like the army. You have someone who tells you what to do. I think we should do it.

B: When is it?
A: At six.
B: Great. So we can go after work.
A: No, it's six in the morning.
B: What?! You must be joking. I hate getting up early. What about doing something later?
A: Well, there's one at lunchtime. It's called Zumba. It's a kind of dance, I think.
B: I don't like dancing.
A: Go on. It looks fun.
B: What about something after work?
A: There's a Pilates class. It doesn't say an exact time but it says it's after work.
B: Well, I'd prefer that to Boot Camp or dancing.
A: Yes, it looks good.

🎧 15
F = Friend, MA = Model answer
F: Are you interested in Boot Camp?
MA: No, I wouldn't like to do it.
F: Go on. You'd enjoy it. It's before work at six in the morning.
MA: I hate getting up early.
F: What about joining the Zumba class? It's a kind of dancing.
MA: I'm not very good at dancing.
F: Pilates sounds good. You should do it with me.
MA: Yes, I'd prefer that to Boot Camp or Zumba.

Unit 3

🎧 18
Last year in India, people bought around 1.5 million new cars. This will probably go up to three million a year in the next few years. That's how the Indian economy is changing. Many Indians in the big cities are richer than ever and they want to spend money on new products. However, most of the money is still in the big cities. There is still a lot of poverty in the villages and countryside.

Now the government hopes a new road in India can help to change India's economy. The Golden Quadrilateral road or GQ connects the country's four biggest cities: Delhi, Mumbai, Chennai and Kolkata. Hopefully, the road will carry business from the giant cities to the smaller and poorer villages and the other half of India's population.

The GQ is nearly 6,000 kilometres long and the most hi-tech highway in the world. At the administration headquarters in Delhi, you can watch thousands of vehicles moving around the country on a computer screen. If there is a problem anywhere with the road, electronic sensors tell the headquarters and engineers instantly drive there.

When you drive on the highway, there is every kind of transport. There are animals pulling carts, motorcycles, lines of old trucks and fast-moving modern cars. Sometimes the road goes right through the middle of a city, so there are often traffic jams and pedestrians trying to cross the six lanes. Industry is also growing along the new highway. When a large company opens a factory, lots of other smaller factories and offices also open. Trucks then drive and deliver all over India along the new highway. For India, all this is a symbol of the country's future.

20

Conversation 1
A: Hi. Do you go to the centre?
B: Which part?
A: Near the cinema.
B: Yes, we stop outside it.
A: Great. Can I have a return ticket, please?

Conversation 2
A: I'd like a first-class ticket, please.
B: That's twenty euros fifty.
A: Here you are. Which platform is it?
B: It's at five fifteen from platform twelve.

Conversation 3
A: How many bags are you checking in?
B: Two. And I've got a carry-on.
A: I'm afraid your ticket only includes one bag. You'll have to pay an extra ten pounds for that one.
B: Oh, OK. Can I pay by credit card?
A: Sure.

Conversation 4
A: It's just up here on the right. You can drop me off over there.
B: I can't stop there. It's a bus stop. But here's OK.
A: OK. How much is that?
B: That's thirteen dollars thirty cents. Have you got the right change?

21

Person 1: What kind of train ticket would you like?
MA: Return, please.
Person 2: Are you checking in any bags today?
MA: Yes, this one.
Person 3: Are you paying by credit card?
MA: No, with cash.
Person 4: It's three euros twenty. Have you got the right change?
MA: Yes, I do. Here you are.
Person 5: Where does your train leave from?
MA: Platform nine.

22

Message 1
Get on the number 68 bus from the bus stop outside your house. Take it to the underground station. Catch the first train and get off at Oxford Road station. Then call me. I'll come and get you.

Message 2
My flight is late and I'm still in Berlin. Don't wait for me at the airport. I'll catch the bus to the city centre and walk to your house. See you later.

Message 3
Chris wants to meet us tonight, so please can you call him and tell him where to meet us. And send me the address of the restaurant as well. What time do you want to meet?

Unit 4

24

Across: 2 patient, 5 hard-working, 6 intelligent, 7 experienced
Down: 1 friendly, 3 positive, 4 kind

25

I = Interviewer, D = Daniel
I: Could you walk through the jungle and survive? One man who knows all about this is rainforest conservationist Doctor Daniel Fanning. Daniel led a team through the Amazonian rainforest. Together they walked for six months. Daniel is here today to explain how he prepares for this kind of expedition.
D: Well, I think preparation is probably the most important part of any expedition. I spent about three months getting ready for this trip. I tested equipment for the walk. For example, I needed to know if the tents could survive the difficult conditions in the rainforests.
I: So, how much did you have to carry in the end? For example, how much clothing did you take?
D: Humans don't really need clothes in the rainforest. It's hot so I recommend shorts and a good raincoat.
I: But don't you need good walking boots?
D: The problem is that you get lots of sand, mud and water inside the boot – especially when it rains, which is nearly all the time. So a pair of sandals is fine. Food and water are the most important things to carry.
I: I was wondering about that. What did you eat?
D: Food like rice is good, but you lose a lot of weight when you walk. I lost about twenty kilos.
I: And one final question. We've talked about the physical side of walking in the jungle, but what about the mental side?
D: Well, you're with other people, but yes you're on your own for long periods of time. But that's good for you I think. It's like a kind of meditation. I also think a journey like this is about determination. I knew that nothing would stop me from reaching the end. So the mind is as important as the body on an expedition.

26

One day, Yossi Ghinsberg started a journey with three other men. They were travelling through the jungle of Bolivia, but after a few days, they were lost. In the end, two of the group, Yossi and Kevin, built a raft so they could travel down the river and find help.

For some time they travelled down the river, but suddenly they hit a rock. Yossi fell off the raft and swam to the shore.

While Yossi was lost in the jungle, his friend Kevin was luckier. He stayed on the raft and luckily some local men found him. Then they searched for Yossi and, amazingly, after three weeks, they found him alive. Sadly, the other two men never returned.

29

F = Friend, MA = Model answer
F: I had a terrible journey into work this morning.
MA: Why?
F: My car broke down on the motorway.
MA: Oh no!
F: Anyway I called the police immediately.
MA: That was a good idea!
F: Luckily, while I was calling, a police car drove past and stopped to help me.
MA: That was lucky!
F: Anyway, they called the garage to get my car and then they brought me to work!
MA: Wow!

Unit 5

🎵 30

It's estimated that the building industry produces around 40% of the world's carbon emissions, which cause climate change. At the same time, the world population is growing, so more people need houses to live in and buildings to work in. So how can we manage the need for houses and the need to reduce carbon emissions?

One way is to design new types of houses that aren't bad for the environment. Take the cardboard house from Holland. That's right. I said cardboard. The house is made from thick, strong cardboard with wood on the inside. It comes in pieces 1.2 metres wide, so it's easy to transport and it takes just one day to build it. The cardboard is covered in a plastic cover so the house stays up in the rain. At the end of its life, you can recycle all of it.

Another recyclable material is glass, and some people are trying to build houses out of glass bottles, though it isn't a new idea. In about 1905 a man called Tom Kelly built a house made with 51,000 glass bottles. The air inside the bottles is an excellent way to keep a comfortable temperature.

And if you don't like the idea of living under cardboard or glass, then you could choose a more traditional building, but have 'living walls' on the outside. In London, one hotel has covered a wall with more than 10,000 plants, and in Milan in Italy they are growing forests on the sides of two towers. The tall buildings will have 900 plants and trees on the sides which will improve Milan's air quality. The forests also protect the people living there from the noise and heat of the city.

🎵 32

Now, on to environmental news. A new report has some interesting facts and figures on how much rubbish a house in America produces. Together, American households produce 243 billion kilos of trash. About 82 billion kilos of this – that's about a third – was made into compost or it was recycled. For individual households, that means about 0.7 kilogrammes was recycled out of nearly two kilos.

As for electronics, the average American household owns 24 electronic devices. These are mostly mobile phones, music players, laptops and computers, and digital cameras. Households with three or more people often own as many as 32 devices, while smaller households own around 17 devices. Recycling more of these items could have a big effect. For example, recycling one million mobile phones can produce 3,500 kilos of gold. Recycling one million computers helps to stop greenhouse gases. It's about the same as taking 16,000 cars off the road.

In 2009, the amount of paper recovered for recycling averaged 150 kilos per person in the United States, or about 380 kilos for each household. Paper recycling has become successful in the US because about 268 million people, or about 87 per cent of American households, now have paper recycling projects nearby.

🎵 33

R = Customer Care Representative, C = Customer
R: Good morning. Can I help you?
C: Hi, I'm calling about a product on your website. I'd like to order it but the website won't let me.
R: One moment ... Do you have the item number?
C: Yes it's 7786–P.
R: So that 7786–P. OK. Is that the garden composter?
C: Yes, that's right.

R: Well, I can take your order by phone.
C: OK, but how much does it cost?
R: Hmm. Can I put you on hold for a moment?
C: Sure. …
R: Hello?
C: Yes, hello.
R: Hi, it's twenty-two pounds.
C: Does that include delivery?
R: Yes, it does.
C: OK. I'll order it.
R: Right. I'll need to take some details. Can I take your surname?
C: It's Bruce. B–R–U–C–E.
R: And the address?
C: 31 Windmill Avenue. And that's in Oxford.
R: Which credit card would you like to pay with?
C: VISA, and the number is 4456 8938 9604 9500.
R: Sorry, is that 9500 at the end?
C: Yes, that's right.
R: Would you like confirmation by email?
C: Yes, please. My email is bob dot bruce fifty one at email dot com.
R: Let me check: bob dot bruce fifty one at email dot com
C: That's right.
R: Is there anything else I can help you with today?
C: No, thanks. That's everything.
R: OK. Goodbye.
C: Bye.

🎵 34

Hello. Can I help you?
Do you have the item number?
Can I take your surname?
Which credit card would you like to pay with?
Can I take the card number?
Would you like confirmation by email?
Can I have your email address?
Is there anything else I can help you with today?
Goodbye.

Unit 6

🎵 37

A = Boss, B = Colleague 1, C = Colleague 2
A: OK everyone. Thanks for coming. The reason I wanted to keep the meeting secret was because, as you know, Rosemary is retiring from the company on Friday and so we're going to have a small leaving party for her.
B: Sorry, but where are we going to have a party? The offices are big but they aren't a very good place to … well, to have fun.
C: That new restaurant next door is good. It's called Zeno's. They serve pizzas and Italian food.
B: Oh, yes. I went there last week.
A: Sounds good. There are going to be about twenty of us. Can someone call the restaurant and find out?
C: I'll do it! I'll call them this afternoon and see what they say.
A: Great.
B: So, who are we going to invite? Just staff? What about wives, husbands, boyfriends, girlfriends as well?
A: Oh no. Only the people she works with.
C: What time is everyone going to meet there?
A: Straight after work. At five.
B: But I'm working late on Friday.
A: Well, between five and six then. We also need to get her a present.
C: Oh yes! What are we going to give her? Oh, I know, she loves plants and I think she's going to spend a lot of time gardening when she retires.
A: Good idea. A plant.

C: And I think we should have a special cake as well.
A: Will the restaurant make us one?
C: Erm, I'm not sure. I'll ask them.
A: Great. Anything else?
B: Look out! She's coming back from her lunch.

38
1 Don't worry. I'll pay.
2 I am going to help Max later.
3 Shelley is coming too.
4 He'll be eighteen years old tomorrow.
5 They are going to travel round the world.
6 Why aren't you watching the parade?

39
Tomorrow our town will be two hundred years old. We are going to have a huge celebration. We plan to have a street parade with costumes and masks. Local musicians are going to play traditional music and at midnight there are going to be fireworks!

40
In New Mexico, the Indian tribe of Mescalero Apaches prepares for a special ceremony every year. Beginning on the 4th July, a group of young Apache girls will spend four days taking part in an ancient ritual which tests their strength and character. By the end of the ritual, they will be women. Preparations begin with each family of the girls making food for many guests and members of the local tribe.

Nearby the men start to build a special tepee. The girls will live in this for the four days.

The ritual begins on the first day at sunrise. The girls run towards the morning sun and then they run round a basket of food four times. Each time represents the four stages of their life: infant, child, teenager and adult woman.

Then they live in the tepee, where they don't have much food. This is part of their test of strength and they must not show any emotions during this period. On the last night, they start to dance. This dance lasts over ten hours through the night and they cannot stop.

On the final morning, the girls come out of the tepee for the last time. They have white clay on their faces, which they slowly wipe off. The tepee falls to the ground and they are now women. The girls receive a new name and their family and friends come to the girls and they celebrate their new status, as women.

41
Conversation 1
S = Sonia, M = Mihaela
S: Hi Mihaela. It's me. Sonia.
M: Hi Sonia. How are you? How was your holiday?
S: Great thanks. But I'm at work so I can't talk long. Do you want to meet after work?
M: Yes, OK. Do you mean tonight?
S: Yes. How about meeting outside my office? We could go to that new Lebanese restaurant on the corner of Main Street.
M: It sounds great. Oh, I've just remembered. I have a friend from France staying. He's doing a language course at the college near me.
S: That's OK. Why don't you invite him as well?
M: That would be great. I'll do that.
S: OK. See you later.
M: Bye.

Conversation 2
P = Phillipe, M = Mihaela
P: Hello?
M: Phillipe. It's Mihaela.
P: Oh hi, Mihaela.
M: Where are you at the moment?
P: I'm about to go into my lesson.
M: Oh. OK. I'll be quick. I'm meeting a close friend of mine tonight and I'd like to take you to meet her.
P: It's very nice of you to ask, but I'm busy tonight. I have an exam tomorrow so I need to revise at home.
M: Are you sure? We're going to eat at a new restaurant. We could get home early or you could study first and come out later.
P: Honestly, I'd love to, but I'm afraid this exam is really important.
M: I completely understand. But if you change your mind, give me a call. OK?
P: OK. And thanks for asking me.
M: See you later.

42
F = Friend, MA = Model answer
Invitation 1
F: Do you want to go to the cinema tonight?
MA: Sorry, I can't because I'm going to a football match tonight.
F: How about going to the cinema tomorrow night instead?
MA: OK. That'd be great.

Invitation 2
F: Would you like to come to a friend's wedding party?
MA: It's very nice of you to ask, but isn't it only for your friend's family and close friends?
F: But I'd like to take you. You'd enjoy it.
MA: OK. I'd like that very much. Thank you.

Unit 7

44
Person 1
I've lived here for five years. I moved here to work for the oil company. I think it's been good for the area. Before, there was nothing here. Now lots of people have moved here and they've built new towns.

Person 2
I've always lived in this area. It was a beautiful place, but then the oil companies came here. In my opinion, they've polluted the rivers and have changed the area forever.

48
Person 1
We are digging this area to build a dam. It will help our village because we need more water. Everyone in the village helps. Today I'm digging with the women from the village. It's really hard work.

Person 2
There's so much to learn because all the computer programs are new for me. In my last job I worked with a different system, but it's always good to learn something new. And everyone seems friendly and helpful here.

Person 3
I've applied for another position. I don't think my current job is very challenging. In fact it's really boring and I've heard that working in the marketing department upstairs is more interesting.

Person 4

I've been here for twenty years. That's right. I've always done the same job and worked for the same company. Not many people can say that anymore. I think it's because I love the place. I like the people I work with and every day there's something interesting to deal with. Why would I change my job?

Person 5

It's always hard to find the right person these days. Especially because our work is so specialized here, so not many people have the right kind of qualifications. We usually have to provide lots of training. Anyway, this week we're interviewing again for two positions, so maybe we'll be lucky.

49

A = Interviewer, B = Candidate
A: Right. Have a seat.
B: Thanks.
A: Right then, I've received your CV and your letter of application. We also received references from your previous employers, which were very positive.
B: That's nice to hear.
A: Now as you know, we're looking for a new receptionist and according to your CV you currently do the same job at a hotel?
B: Well, I work at the front desk, so I think a lot of the skills are similar. You know, welcoming people, answering the phone, dealing with any problems that come up.
A: Yes, that's interesting. How long have you worked in your current position?
B: I've been there for about a year.
A: And why do you want to leave? Why have you applied for this position?
B: Well, I like working at the hotel, but I'm more interested in working for a business like yours.
A: I see. Would you describe yourself as ambitious?
B: Yes, I suppose I am a little. Though really, I like learning new things and working with different people.
A: So, do you work well in a team?
B: Yes, I think so.
A: Can you give me an example of when you have worked with other people?
B: Err, well. OK, yes. Recently, we had a conference at our hotel, so there was lots to arrange. The hotel manager was very ill that week, so all of us on reception had to help with everything. It was great because none of us had organized anything like that before, so it was a real challenge. But the guests were all happy and the feedback to the hotel was very good. It was a real team effort.
A: That's very good. So, what are some of your other strengths?
B: Err. I work hard and I enjoy working with other people. And … er … I can solve problems.
A: Could you tell me more about that? What's an example of a recent problem you solved …
Well, I've asked you a lot of questions. Do you have any questions for me?
B: Yes, I do. Would I receive any training?
A: Well, we have a receptionist who is moving to a different department, but she would work with you for a few weeks. So, yes there's training, but it's on-the-job training mainly.
B: I see.

50

I = Interviewer, MA = Model answer
I: How long have you worked in your current job?

MA: I've been there since 2008.
I: Would you describe yourself as ambitious?
MA: I suppose so. I like hard work and I'd like to become successful in my career.
I: What are some of your main strengths?
MA: I enjoy working in a team. I think I'm good with other people.
I: Do you have any weaknesses?
MA: Sometimes I work too hard. I don't know when to stop.
I: What's the most difficult thing you have ever done?
MA: Once I was in charge of some colleagues and it was difficult to tell them what to do.
I: How well do you work with other people?
MA: As I said before, I like working in teams and I think people like working with me.
I: Can you give me an example of how you have solved a problem at work?
MA: Let me think. Well, once we had a customer. She wasn't happy with the service and I had to deal with the problem.

Unit 8

51

A: What's the problem?
B: I've never used this GPS before and I'm having trouble getting a signal.
A: If it's raining, it always has a problem. Let me try … There, I think I've got it. And then if you want our location, press the button with a star. Press it again if you want a closer view.
B: OK. Great.
A: What are you looking for exactly?
B: The helicopter pilot left a message earlier. He wants to know where to pick us up. I think the nearest place is here.
A: Hmm. It's about two days away.
B: Yes, but if he flies closer to us, he won't find anywhere to land. There are too many trees.
A: What about here? It looks flat. If we walk all day tomorrow, we might get there by the evening.
B: Maybe, if the weather's good. If it isn't, then we'll try to leave the day after. … Oh! What happened? It's gone!
A: The battery needs recharging.

53

Good morning. Today I'd like to talk about the technology of biometrics. First of all, what is biometrics? Biometrics is the science of a person's appearance or behaviour. So for example, human beings all have an individual physical appearance. They've got different eyes and different hair. And everyone has a different way of walking or moving. So we can also study their behaviour.

So how can we use biometrics? Well, it's very useful in the area of security. At the moment if you travel through an airport, you need your identity card or passport. If you go to your bank to get some money, you need a card and a special number. But what if you lose your passport? What if you forget your number?

Biometric technology can solve this problem. Your biometric information is your fingerprint, for example. If you press your finger onto a screen, the technology can read the fingerprint and check your identity. Airports already use similar technology which looks inside your eye and also checks your identity. Biometric technology can also recognize your voice and your movements.

Finally, are there any problems with this technology? Well, it's very expensive, so you'll only see it in places like airports, banks or government offices. Sometimes the technology can make mistakes and it's not always correct. However, in the future, the technology will get cheaper and more effective, so it will become more and more important in our everyday lives.

🎵 54
Conversation one
A: What is this for?
B: It's for filming things when you're climbing.
A: Really? How does it work?
B: Well, you put the small round camera on your helmet. Then this bit goes on your belt.
A: Where do I switch it on?
B: You press the red button.
A: Oh, I see. Hey! That's very cool.
B: Yes, it's really easy to use.
A: How long does the battery last?
B: I'm not sure, but quite a few hours. So you can take it with you up a mountain, for example. Then when you get home, you just plug it straight into the TV.

Conversation two
A: I can't make this work.
B: Let me have a look … Here you go.
A: How did you do that?
B: I pressed the red button.
A: Oh. What happens if I press this other button?
B: It moves the map around. Look. And I can press this as well.
A: Why do you need to do that?
B: It shows your location and the place you want to go to.
A: I see. Oh one more thing. How do you switch it off?
B: Hold the red button down for five seconds.

🎵 56
F = friend, MA = model answer
F: I've bought this video camera to fix to my drone. So now I can make videos from the air!
MA: Really? How does it work?
F: Well, the camera fits underneath the drone, and you use this remote control. So I think you press this button to start filming …
MA: I see.
F: The other thing you can do is take it off the drone and use it like a normal camera. And you can even use it to take photos underwater.
MA: That's very cool.
F: But I don't understand how to switch it on. Where's the on button?
MA: Let me have a look.

Unit 9

🎵 57
F = Friend, W = Woman
F: How was your holiday?
W: A disaster!
F: Why?
W: Well, it had looked great on the website, and there were mountains next to the cottage, so there was plenty of space for the children to play and nice long walks in the nearby forest with the dog.
F: So what was the problem?
W: First of all, we arrived late at night after a ten-hour drive. It's normally three hours from London, but there'd been a delay on the motorway. I woke up a few times because I thought I heard someone in the house. Then in the morning, my daughter said there were clothes in her chest of drawers. She was right. It was full of clothes.
F: How strange!

W: Anyway, we took the clothes out and put them in a box and we drove to a beach about two miles away. But when we got back, the clothes were back in the chest of drawers and my daughter's clothes were in the box.
F: Really? So someone was there with you?
W: Well, later in the afternoon I saw a light at the end of a field and there was a shed. A man was living in it! And guess what?
F: What?
W: He owned the cottage, but he always lived in the shed. But he said he kept his clothes in the house and asked us not to move them. I couldn't believe it!
F: So what did you do?
W: Well, we stayed for the rest of the week and never saw him again. But I wouldn't go back there.

🎵 59
I had an amazing time with a tour group in Morocco. On the first day, our tour guide showed us round the centre of Marrakesh. First, we went to the square in the middle of the city called the Jemaa El Fna. It's a fascinating place where people sell things, old men play musical instruments and there are people with snakes! Actually we were a bit worried about the snakes and moved away when we saw them come towards us on the ground. After a day walking round the city, everyone was tired, so we relaxed at the hotel and ate great food.

The next day was exciting because we went by bus up the Atlas Mountains. The views were incredible as we went up, although the bus driver drove too fast for me. I was a bit frightened on some of the high roads, but we safely reached the top and then the road went down to a region of green fields. We finally arrived at a small hotel, and I was surprised because it looked ugly on the outside. But after we walked through a large gate, the owners met us with a smile and showed us round their beautiful hotel with its huge swimming pool and orange trees.

🎵 61
I = Interviewer, S = Stella
I: Good afternoon and welcome to the *Travel Show*. This week our travel correspondents are reporting back from the beaches of Thailand and a walking adventure in the Pyrenees mountains. But first, many of you write to us every week for holiday advice and perhaps one of the most common questions is: *How much do I tip in other countries?* Well, to help us this week we have travel journalist, Stella Swan. So, Stella, is there a rule on tipping that's true for everywhere you travel or is it always different?
S: Well, the only rule I'd say is pay a tip when you are really happy with the service. I also tip the people who make a difference to my holiday.
I: How do you mean?
S: Well, if I'm staying at a hotel, I'll always leave a nice tip for the cleaning staff. They probably get paid the lowest wage in the hotel, but they are the people who look after your room, so you want them to do a good job.
I: OK, so which country expects the highest tips?
S: I think most people are surprised in North America where twenty per cent is considered normal.
I: That does seem like a lot.
S: Maybe, but in Canada and the USA you also pay a little less at the restaurant and the hotel, but you get good service in return. If you don't get good service, then leave ten per cent.

I: What about in central or south America? Is it also twenty?
S: It tends to be lower. Around ten per cent is normal.
I: Yes, in my experience ten per cent is fairly standard. Especially in European countries.
S: I think it is, although in places like China or Japan, it isn't common to tip at all. It also depends on where you are. So in the USA, you tip for everything in a hotel whereas I wouldn't tip so much elsewhere. The other thing to remember is that many restaurants and hotels include a service charge.
I: Yes, I've noticed that. I was in a restaurant in India and the bill included ten percent so I didn't tip.
S: I think that's more and more normal in lots of countries. Especially in places where there are lots of people from different countries. It solves the problem.

62
TO = Tourist information office, T = Tourist
TO: Hello? Can I help you?
T: I'm interested in visiting the history museum. Do you know the opening times?
TO: Sure. Let me check. Today is Monday, so I'm afraid it's closed all day. But it's open from Tuesday to Sunday. So it's open tomorrow.
T: Great. What time does it open?
TO: At nine-thirty and it closes at five-thirty.
T: Oh right. Could you tell me the price?
TO: It's free.
T: Oh, that's good. Are there any other museums which are open today?
TO: We have a science museum but that's closed as well today. How about going to the art gallery across the road?
T Um, I'm not sure. How much is that?
TO: It's free for the general exhibition and five euros for the special exhibitions. You can also take an interesting guided tour at midday. It's also five euros.
T: Well, OK. That might be good.
TO: You can buy the ticket for the tour at the entrance.
T: One other thing. On Wednesday I want to visit the national park outside the town. Is there any public transport there?
TO: A bus leaves the bus station at ten in the morning and returns at five. Another option is to take a taxi. It isn't too expensive.

63
TI = Tourist information officer, MA = Model answer
TI: Hello, how can I help you?
MA: I'm interested in visiting the city castle. Do you know the opening times?
TI: Yes, it's open every day from ten till six.
MA: Great. Could you tell me the price?
TI: It's seven euros.
MA: Is there a bus?
TI: Yes, take bus 15 from the station.
MA: How often does it leave?
TI: Every fifteen minutes.

Unit 10

64
The plant called papyrus was grown by the ancient Egyptians. It was produced to make boats, baskets, boxes, tables, sandals and many other products. However, it was most famous as a writing tool in Egypt and later it was used by the Romans. The inside of the long plant was cut into pieces. These pieces were put across each other and dried. Nowadays, paper is rarely made from papyrus but the plant is still used in building materials.

66
Conversation 1
A: I love your new bag. Did you buy it in Italy?
B: No, actually I bought it online, but I think it's made in Vietnam. There's a great website that sells bags from all over the world. You should take a look. They're much cheaper than on the high street.
A: Great. Can you give me the address?

Conversation 2
A: What do you think? Do you like it?
B: Hmm, it's nice, but a bit old-fashioned. What about the blue dress?
A: Really?
B: I know it's quite basic, but it's a classic look.

Conversation 3
A: Dad, did you use to listen to music on records or cassettes?
B: Neither. I'm not that old! The first music I bought was on CD. I used to buy a new CD every month.
A: What did you do with them?
B: I think they're probably in a box somewhere. Nowadays I download all my music.

Conversation 4
A: Does this stuff on my desk belong to you?
B: What stuff?
A: Books, paper and pens and some other things.
B: Oh that. It all belongs to Jim.
A: Where is he? I'd like him to move it.
B: He's probably at lunch.

Conversation 5
A: Can I ask you a few questions as part of a survey?
B: Sure, go ahead.
A: How many times a day do you check your social media on your phone?
B: I'd say around twenty times a day. Or thirty maybe.

Conversation 6
A: In my opinion, we have too much stuff in our houses these days. We don't need it all.
B: I see what you mean, but I think people will have fewer things in the future because so much of our life will be online. For example, I'm going to sell my TV and radio because I don't use them anymore. I use my tablet to watch films or listen to radio. So I think it will change.

67
M = Manager, K = Katarina
M: What do you think about our new website Katarina?
K: It's good but I think we should add a blog.
M: That's interesting. Why do you think that?
K: Well, in my opinion, customers like reading news on websites. So we can have news about our products.
M: I agree, but I think that sort of thing can go on the website with advertisements.
K: I'm not sure about adverts because people don't look at them. People will read about products if it's a blog post and not an advert.
M: I see what you mean, but what would you write about?
K: Maybe we could have interviews with customers who use our products.
M: Good idea.

K: Or we could have photos of our employees in their free time – something fun.
M: You're right. I suggest you write the first post and we can see if people read it.

68
C = Colleague, MA = Model answer
C: Why don't we make a website to sell our products?
MA: Good idea!
C: I think we should design it as soon as possible.
MA: I agree.
C: It needs different pages. What do you think?
MA: I think we should have a home page and then some product pages.
C: You're right. Do you have any other suggestions?
MA: Maybe we could have some pictures of our employees.

69
advert, advertisement, advertising, advertise, produce, production, productive, product, invent, invention, inventor, sell, sold, sales

Unit 11

70
Speaker 1
I think the first time I saw it I was sitting in a library and someone was sending an email. That was in about 1990. I'm sure people used it before that but I hadn't seen it until then. By the end of the twentieth century it was fairly common. Now everyone uses it.

Speaker 2
I wasn't born in 1945 but my grandparents used to talk about it. There were parties in the streets and people celebrated after five long years. They'd lost friends and neighbours, so it isn't the kind of thing you forget.

Speaker 3
I remember it really well because I was there in 1987. I walked out the hotel and there were lines of people all waiting. I followed them to see what they were doing. In the distance you could see the yellow symbol. I don't think many people had eaten American fast food before so there was a lot of excitement.

Speaker 4
OK, so that was in 1969 and I was about ten years old. I remember my family didn't have a television so we went to our cousins'. My aunt and uncle had more money than us! The pictures weren't great, but I'll never forget hearing the famous words 'one giant leap for mankind'. None of us could believe it!

Speaker 5
As soon as it happened, I packed my bags and took a train across Europe to Germany. I wanted to be one of the first people to get a piece of it. I was a student in 1989 and I missed some of my classes. I got into a lot of trouble, but it was worth it for a piece of history.

71
1 I love this video game.
2 Lizzie, I left a message on your phone.
3 We'll meet you later.
4 Peter, I'm sending you an email.
5 They've put a job advert in the newspaper.
6 Your picture is on Facebook, Sally.

73
About two hours north of London by train is one of England's oldest cities. The city of York is about halfway between London and Scotland, so every year thousands of tourists stop off here to visit this beautiful city. It's famous for the cathedral, the museums, and the ancient streets with lots of traditional shops and good places to eat.

Modern York is a peaceful and relaxing city, but its history was often violent. When the early Romans first arrived in England they needed a place for their armies to stay in the north. They started building in the city in 71 AD. You can still walk along parts of the ancient Roman walls around the old city. Eventually, the local people fought the Romans and they left England. For a while people lived in the city or visited to buy and sell their food.

However, the Vikings from what is now Norway and Sweden arrived in England in the ninth century. At first, they attacked and stole from the people in the area. Later, some Vikings started to live in York. A thousand years later, in the 1980s, archaeologists began to discover Viking objects beneath the centre of York. You can see many of these objects in the city's Viking museum, including statues and pots for cooking.

After the Vikings, William the Conqueror came with his army from Normandy, in northern France, and took the country. He became King of England in 1066. Like the Romans, William used York as a centre for his army in the north and he built a castle here. He also started building a church called York Minster. Since then, York Minster has been rebuilt and made bigger. Today, it is one of England's most important religious buildings.

74
Hello, and thank you for coming. Today I would like to talk about my gap year in Vietnam. First I'll describe my first few days there. Then I'll move on to my job there and I'll show you some of my photos. Finally, I'll talk about my journeys through the country and describe my experiences of the culture. So let's begin …

So that's everything I wanted to say about the first few days. Now let's move on to the kind of work I was doing. We'll take a look at this photo. It shows you the school I worked in and all the children …

OK. So the final part of my presentation is about my journeys. I travelled a bit at weekends but I also took a longer journey in the last month of my gap year. So I'd like to show you some of my photos from that period and I'll read a few comments from my diary …

Right. That's the end of my talk. As you can see, I had an amazing few months and, to sum up, I'd recommend it to anyone. We have about ten minutes left, so are there any questions?

Unit 12

75
P = Presenter, C = Claire
P: Today I'm walking in some beautiful countryside about twenty kilometres from the city of San Francisco. It's very peaceful here with a few wild animals and trees. But in fact I'm standing on something quite dangerous, because I'm walking along the San Andreas Fault. It's a huge fault line which goes right through the state of California. Now to help me understand the San Andreas Fault, I'm with Claire Hands who is a geologist, and she specializes in the study of earthquakes and in the San Andreas Fault in particular. So Claire, we're standing right on the fault. What would happen if the fault opened right now?

C: Well, if it opened and there was an earthquake, we'd probably fall over. It'd be really difficult to stand up because the ground would be moving. But if we were standing in the countryside like we are now, we'd probably be safer than anyone would be in a city like San Francisco.

P: Right. Because of all the buildings falling down.

C: That's right. And the fault line goes right through the centre of San Francisco, so an earthquake would be really bad news for anyone living there.

P: And that has happened, hasn't it?

C: Yes, the most famous earthquake in San Francisco was in 1906. There have been lots of smaller earthquakes or tremors in California since then but nothing as big as that one.

P: So, it is possible to guess when an earthquake will happen?

C: Scientists and especially geologists would like to be able to do that. We understand a lot about earthquakes and there is equipment which monitors them. We can predict where they will happen and possibly how big they will be. The problem is 'when'. We can't predict when they will happen. If we knew this, we could make a much bigger difference.

79

1
The artist Georgia O'Keefe is probably best-known for paintings of flowers and natural habitats. This painting is typical of her work. It's a mountain range in New Mexico where she lived later in her life. She called it the 'White Place' and she painted it many times.

2
We're in for a cold period over the next week with temperatures as low as minus two or three degrees. On higher ground we'll see snow and on Tuesday there might be some hail in some parts of the country. By the end of the week things will warm up again and any snow will turn into rain, making roads dangerous, so drive carefully.

3
R= reporter, M = man

R: Following the news that a gorilla escaped from a zoo at the weekend, a lot of people have complained about the conditions in modern zoos. To test public opinion, we interviewed some people in the street.

R: Hello? Can we ask you about the gorilla that escaped this weekend?

M: Where was that?

R: It was in your city zoo. Someone left the door open and the gorilla escaped. Don't worry, they caught it again in the end.

M: Poor thing. I think they should let the poor animals go and close the zoo.

R: Why do you think that?

M: They're wild animals so they need to live in the wild, not locked up…

4
Looking for something to do with the family this weekend? Come and visit Everson's Zoo. Say hello to the lions and meet the elephants. You can also learn more about our conservation programme for leopards. You can have lunch in the wildlife café and the children will love playing in the 'animal adventure' park. Take advantage of our weekend ticket offer today and for the price of two adults, up to three children go for free.

5
I = interviewer, P = Patrick

I: Today I'm talking to someone who calls themselves a stormchaser. His name is Patrick McHugh.

P: Hello.

I: Welcome to the show. So Patrick, let me tell the people out there what you do. You follow tornadoes around the United States. Most people drive away from tornadoes, so what makes you do it?

P: It's exciting and you never get bored of the power of nature when you see a tornado. But I'm also a professional photographer so it's about getting as close as you can and then trying to get the best picture …

80

A: OK. Thank you for coming. So, as you know, we have this area in the south-east of the city with old buildings and a factory which has been closed for over ten years. It used to be an industrial area, but now there are new houses in the area with people living there and a local school. So we are going to pull down all the old buildings and do something with the area.

B: It's a nice idea but the council doesn't have any money this year. I'm sorry, but we can't afford more new projects.

C: What about selling the land for more housing?

B: That's a good idea.

A: Yes, but we have lots of land for housing. And anyway, I think local people want somewhere to relax.

B: I see. Well, why don't we make it into a park or something?

A: I agree. That's also what I was thinking.

C: We could also have a lake there.

A: How do you mean?

B: Well, when they clear away the buildings they could dig a small lake. It would attract wildlife to the area.

A: That isn't a bad idea. I like it.

B: We might suggest the idea to the local people.

C: And we could ask school children at the local school to design the park.

A: Nice idea, but I think this needs some professional help.

B: No, that won't work. We don't have any money to pay them. I think we need local volunteers from the community to help …

C: Yes, you might be right.

A: So, let's summarize what we've agreed so far. We all agree that it's a good idea to clear the area, but not to build anything on it. We want to build a park or green space for local people to relax in.

B: And perhaps with a lake.

A: With a lake. However, we don't have much money for this, so we need to approach the local community and ask for ideas and volunteers …

C: That's right.

81

S = Speaker, MA = Model answer

1
S: How about building a new park for local people?
MA: That's a good idea.

2
S: We could also have a playground for children.
MA: Sounds great!

3
S: And maybe local people could design the park.
MA: I'm not sure.

4
S: What if we asked people to pay money for the park?
MA: No, that won't work.

IELTS practice test

82

Presenter: In this test you'll hear a number of different recordings and you'll have to answer questions on what you hear. There will be time for you to read the instructions and questions, and you will have a chance to check your answers. The recording will be played once only. The test is in four sections.

Now turn to section one on page 100 of your book. You will hear a hotel manager telling an employee called Steffi about her work trip to Australia. First you have time to look at questions 1 and 2. You will see that there is also an example which has been done for you.

Presenter: Now we shall begin. You should answer the questions as you listen, because you will not hear the recording a second time. Listen carefully and answer questions 1 and 2.

Man: Hello, Steffi.

Steffi: Hello.

Man: Thanks for coming. I want to brief you about your trip to Australia.

Steffi: Great. I'm really excited about it.

Man: So, let's see. You'll work at one of the company's hotels in Australia for one month, and you're leaving in a week's time. I'm going to be away myself from tomorrow, so I wanted to make sure you were fully briefed.

Steffi: Thank you.

Man: Now although it's part of the Ambassador group, the hotel you're going to work at is actually called the Bristol. The company's other hotel in Sydney is called the Carlton, by the way – another member of staff went there last year and had a great time.

Steffi: I see.

Man: Now, I know you usually work on reception here, but in a new place that's not a good idea. So for the first few days you will help out in the manager's office – doing general duties. Then later on, you'll work in different areas, including the dining room and the conference centre.

Steffi: Sounds great.

Presenter: Before you listen to the rest of the conversation, you have some time to read questions 3 to 10. Now listen and answer questions 3 to 10.

Steffi: Can I ask about the working hours?

Man: Sure. Now, you do thirty-five hours a week here, but on this kind of work experience placement, you only have to do thirty.

Steffi: Really?

Man: Yes, but it means working five hours a day, six days a week. I hope that's OK for you.

Steffi: Oh, yes. No problem.

Man: And during your stay, you'll do morning, afternoon and evening shifts. That means starting at either seven in the morning, at midday or at five in the evening. For the first week, you'll be on the afternoon shift.

Steffi: Oh, that's good. So I get one day off?

Man: That's right. Obviously in Australia weekends are busy, so you'll work on Saturdays and Sundays, but I've agreed that you'll be free on Fridays. I hope that's alright?

Steffi: Absolutely. Thank you. And will I stay in the hotel itself?

Man: Yes, free accommodation is included – but that's in a shared room. If you want a single room, then you have to pay a little extra – but only a few dollars.

Steffi: Oh yes, I'm sure I'd prefer that.

Man: OK, I'll let them know. Breakfast is provided free of charge in the hotel, but if you want to eat lunch or dinner there, you have to pay.

Steffi: I see. Are there any staff discounts?

Man: Not in the restaurant. But, if you buy anything in the hotel shop, you get 10% off.

Steffi: Right.

Man: There may be other perks I'm not aware of, but you'll have what's called a mentor at the hotel, who can tell you more.

Steffi: Sorry .... what's that?

Man: A mentor. It's a member of staff who's available to give advice and help if you need it. I've got her name here somewhere ... umm. Ah yes, Mrs Drinkstone. That's D-R-I-N-K-S-T-O-N-E. I don't seem to have her first name – but I'll get it for you.

Steffi: Thanks. It all sounds fantastic.

Man: Oh – one last thing. We want to know how the trip goes, what's different about the two hotels from the employee's point of view, positive or negative. So you'll be asked to write a report each week. There's a template available. I'll email it to you.

Steffi: Oh great. Thanks.

Man: So I think that's all. I hope you have a wonderful time.

Steffi: Thank you.

Presenter: Now turn to Section 2 on page 101 of your book. You will hear some information about English language courses. First you have some time to look at questions 11 to 15.

Woman: Thanks for coming to this short presentation about the courses available at the Central Language School in Hanford.

First of all, let me tell you where the language school is. Most people arrive in the city by train, and the station's on the edge of the city-centre area. It's about half-an-hour on foot from there to the main university campus, and the Central Language School can be found just next door. There are frequent buses if you don't fancy the walk.

Because Hanford's a university city, there's plenty of student accommodation. Most university students rent houses which they share with friends. The majority of language school students, however, stay in host-family accommodation, where meals are provided and there's a chance to practise language skills. There are also self-catering rooms available in a student residence, but this works out more expensive, so isn't so popular.

In terms of leisure activities, the school doesn't have tennis courts or anything like that. There's a public park opposite, though, where students can use the football pitch without having to pay. In addition, the school has an arrangement with a local gym, so that students can use its facilities at a discounted price.

Some students prefer to spend their free time in the school library. It has a collection of reference books that can be used on-site, but not taken away. There's also a selection of English-language films on DVD, which students can watch on-site or borrow overnight. There's internet access too. Students get a password and an hour's free use each day – though there's a booking system for busy periods. The library's also got a selection of magazines, which is updated weekly, but daily newspapers are not provided.

Presenter: Before you hear the rest of the presentation, you have some time to look at questions 16 to 20.

Woman: OK – so what about the courses themselves? Basically, there are three courses available. You can study either for fifteen hours per week, for eighteen hours per week, or for twenty-one hours per week. Let me tell you about the three different courses.

Students on the fifteen-hour course study General English and come to school in the morning only, leaving the afternoons free for self-study or free-time activities. There are twelve students in the class, and there are classes at four different levels. Students do an entry test on arrival, to see which level is best for them. The price of this course is £430 per week.

The eighteen-hour course combines general English with exam preparation. This has the same programme as the 15-hour course, with the addition of special exam preparation sessions four afternoons a week; that is, each weekday with the exception of Friday. This course is suitable for those doing an exam at some time in the future. There are ten students in the class and this course costs £465 per week.

Finally, we have intensive exam preparation courses. These are more expensive at £495. There are only eight students in the class, all preparing to do the exam in the near future. As well as 21 class hours, each student has a personal tutorial once a week.

So that's our school. Before I go on, does anyone have any questions?

Presenter: Now turn to Section 3 on page 102 of your book. You will hear two students called Adam and Becky talking about a traffic survey they have to do as part of their college course. First you have some time to look at questions 21 to 26.

Adam: Hi Becky.
Becky: Hi Adam.
Adam: So we're going to be working together on the traffic survey – that'll be fun.
Becky: Yeah, I'm really looking forward to it. I guess we should start making some plans. Are you free now?
Adam: Sure. Where shall we begin? The idea is to do some research into local road traffic, isn't it?
Becky: That's right. On the worksheet it says we've got to choose one important place on the local road system, count the number of cars using it in a given period, and also try and find out why it's busier at certain times than at others.
Adam: Mmm, sounds interesting. How long have we got?
Becky: Well, we should choose two days in the week – like a weekday and a weekend day and do the survey over a number of weeks – you know, to be sure that we get data that represents an average,

which is based on a sample of days and not just one day that might be unusual for some reason.
Adam: Sure. So that's two days a week for what, three weeks?
Becky: Yes, I reckon that should be enough. I'm free on Mondays if that's alright with you, and then perhaps we should do Saturdays as the contrast.
Adam: Yes, that's good for me too. But do we just set up at the roadside – don't we have to get permission or anything?
Becky: Well, the local police will tell us where is the best place to set up from a safety point of view, and they'll keep an eye on us to make sure there are no problems. But we have to tell them which road we want to do.
Adam: Great. So where should we ask for?
Becky: Well, I thought outside the shopping centre would be a good place. We could count how many cars using the road were going into the centre, and how many drove past it.
Adam: Good idea.
Becky: But we've got to do more than just count the cars, haven't we?
Adam: Yes, we've also got to interview some drivers. So whilst one of us counts the cars, the other one can be in the car park doing the interviews.
Becky: OK. Let's take it in turns to do both these jobs because just counting the cars could get boring.
Adam: I agree. And there are other jobs we could share out too. Somebody's got to prepare the questionnaire we use for the interviews. You're good at writing that sort of thing, Becky. Would you mind doing that?
Becky: I'd be happy to, though we'd need to discuss it a bit first. Then maybe you could save the data on to the laptop at the end of each day.
Adam: OK, yes. What does that involve?
Becky: Well, we're going to have an electronic counter for the cars. You press a button each time one passes, and it records it. Then you put the figures into the database on the laptop at the end of the day.
Adam: OK. I think I could manage that!
Becky: Thanks Adam.

Presenter: Before you hear the rest of the conversation, you have some time to look at questions 27 to 30.

Adam: So, what do you think we should ask in the questionnaire?
Becky: Well, the questionnaire's meant to find out some reasons that explain the data. You know, it's no good saying how many cars use the route at a given time without having some idea of why they do that.
Adam: OK – so the main focus needs to be on why they chose to go by car rather than catch the bus, or go by bike?
Becky: Oh, I'm not sure that's it really. Isn't it more why the drivers chose that route and not another one?
Adam: Umm – well we're only asking the ones who drive into the car park, so I guess we already know that.
Becky: You're right. OK then, I reckon we need to ask them why they chose to travel at that time.
Adam: Yes, OK – that can be the main focus of the questionnaire – various questions about that. But maybe we should ask a supplementary question, to get an idea of the type of people they are.

Becky:	What do you mean?
Adam:	Well, like if we ask them what they think about climate change – then we'd see if they were concerned about green issues or not.
Becky:	That's a good idea. That would tell us more about them than asking them what they think of the car park itself or why they use their cars instead of the bus.
Adam:	Great – let's do that then.
Becky:	Then once we've finished the survey, we've got to write a report which we then present to the class.
Adam:	I think that writing the actual report is a job that's best done by one person – it would be messy trying to join different bits together.
Becky:	I agree. And I'm happy to do that if you like. I mean, I'm sure you'd do it very well, but I'm happier writing things than I am presenting them. If you want to do a draft though, for me to work from, that would be OK. Or I could just show you mine before I write up the final version?
Adam:	Well, there's no point in having two drafts. I'll look at yours and make comments.
Becky:	OK. And you'll do the presentation?
Adam:	Sure. I mean as far as I'm concerned that's the easy part. You're a very good presenter, I know, but that's because you've had a lot more experience than me. It will do me good to do it actually – give me more confidence about speaking in public.
Becky:	Great. That's agreed then.
Presenter:	Now turn to Section 4 on page 103 of your book. You will hear part of a lecture about a type of bird called a red kite, which is found in western Europe. First you have some time to look at questions 31 to 40. Now listen carefully and answer questions 31 to 40.
Woman:	Good evening. Tonight's lecture is about a bird of prey called the red kite. This bird used to be common in the British Isles, but died out in England and Scotland during the nineteenth century. In recent years however, the red kite has been reintroduced to these countries, and it's the story of that programme that I want to tell you about tonight. Firstly, why did the red kite disappear from most of Britain? Well, there are a number of reasons. Many centuries ago, the red kite was a valued bird that helped keep the streets clean by eating

waste food. As cities became cleaner, there was less for the birds to eat, so their numbers began to fall. Some people even killed them because they thought they were dirty. In the nineteenth century, as the kite became rarer, it became a target for people who collected birds' eggs as a hobby. The red kite became extinct in England in 1871 and in Scotland in 1879.

However, people have been trying to help the birds. As long ago as 1903, British people interested in red kite conservation formed a committee to protect the bird. By then there were only a small number of birds left in Wales. Until about 1950, the number of birds did not increase much. This is why a re-introduction programme was needed and plans for this began in the year 1986. The idea was to bring birds living in other countries to England. Red kites were still found in various Western European countries like France and Germany, but in 1989, the first reintroduced birds came from Spain and Sweden. These birds were released in sites in southern England, with a total of ninety-three birds being set free. On the whole, the programme was successful and by 1992, the first pairs of birds had begun breeding in the wild. Indeed the programme was so successful that in 1996 a similar one began in Scotland.

The reintroduction programme was organized following strict rules. These rules say that reintroduction should only be allowed if certain criteria apply. For example, the birds must have disappeared due to human activity rather than through natural causes – that's the first of the criteria. The second one says that there must still be a habitat which is suitable for the birds in the country. If it has disappeared, then reintroduction wouldn't work. Thirdly, the birds which are introduced from another country must be similar genetically to the birds that used to live in the area where they will be released. And finally, the removal of birds from another place mustn't endanger the survival of the species there. Happily, in the case of the red kite's reintroduction to Britain, all these criteria were met.

Consequently, the red kite's future as a British breeding species is now much brighter. There are probably around 1,800 breeding pairs in Britain.

Answer key

Unit 1

1a (pages 4 and 5)

1
1 works   2 specializes   3 goes   4 studies   5 wants
6 spends   7 don't stay   8 travel   9 visit
10 don't realize   11 helps   12 don't have

2
1 starts   2 watches   3 flies   4 passes   5 lives
6 studies   7 finishes   8 relaxes

3
/s/   helps, visits, wants
/z/   has, is, spends, stays, studies, travels
/ɪz/   realizes, specializes

4
1 Where does Nathan work?
2 Where does he often go?
3 What does he find and study?
4 Where does he spend a lot of time?
5 Why do new viruses travel more easily?
6 What does he need for his work?
7 Do people have electricity in every part of the world?
8 How does Nathan communicate?

5
1 c   2 b   3 a   4 a

6
1 I always do exercise in the evening.
2 It is always colder in the winter.
3 I take this medicine twice a day.
4 They don't often go on holiday.
5 We are sometimes busy at weekends.
6 She rarely eats out during the week.
7 You are never on time for work.
8 Do you always check your emails at lunchtime?

1b (pages 6 and 7)

1
1 b   2 c   3 b   4 b   5 c   6 b   7 a

2
1 is responsible for   2 pregnant   3 patient
4 mothers-to-be   5 hospital   6 deliver
7 shortage   8 mobile   9 serious   10 local

3
Today they are visiting their first patient.
Sarubai is checking Rani …
While they are checking the baby …
… and the number is growing.

4
1 I'm driving
2 has
3 do you come
4 is flying
5 I never cycle
6 is standing
7 Do you always leave
8 it's getting
9 aren't staying
10 Are you working; are you taking

5
a 5   b 4   c 3   d 3   e 4   f 4

6
1 living   2 dropping   3 letting   4 swimming   5 having
6 lying   7 taking   8 travelling   9 getting   10 jogging

7
I usually get up at about seven o'clock and go running for
half an hour. Then I feel ready for the day. I leave the house
at about eight thirty and arrive at the hospital by nine.
Currently, I'm seeing lots of children with flu. After work I
often walk home. Sometimes friends come round for dinner,
but I need eight hours of sleep a night so I'm always in bed
by eleven o'clock.

1c (page 8)

1
1 happy   2 money   3 students   4 country

2
1 c   2 b   3 b   4 c   5 a   6 a

3
1 f   2 c   3 b   4 a   5 d   6 e

4
1 e   2 d   3 a   4 c   5 b

5
Possible answers:
Do you feel like a coffee?
Do you feel like doing something?
How do you feel today?
Do you feel OK?
Does it feel cold outside?
What do you feel like doing?

1d (page 9)

1
1 nose   2 ear   3 tooth   4 head   5 throat   6 back
7 mouth   8 stomach

2
1 How does your stomach feel?
2 Is your throat sore or is it better?
3 Drink this hot water.
4 My headache is worse today.
5 Can I see the doctor about my ear?
6 This is good for a runny nose.

3
Tick the following for 1–3:
1 sore throat, cough   2 high   3 pills
4 Advice: Go to bed for two days. Drink lots of water.
Come back if you still feel ill.

4
1 How do you feel
2 Let me have a
3 Do you feel
4 Have you got
5 Let me check
6 take this prescription
7 You need to
8 They are good
9 try drinking
10 If you still feel ill

5
Model answers:
You need to take some pills.
Try taking some hot water with lemon and honey.
Go to bed for a couple of days.
You need to see a doctor.
Take this medicine. It's good for flu.

1e (page 10)

1 title
2 Middle initial
3 D.O.B.
4 Contact no (daytime)
5 General health
6 Previous serious illnesses
7 Number of hours of exercise per week
8 Contact person/number (in case of emergency)
9 Postcode
10 Surname

2

3
Students' own answers.

Wordbuilding / Learning skills (page 11)

1
1 run a marathon
2 go hiking
3 play the piano
4 read a book
5 do exercise
6 take public transport
7 check … emails
8 have a coffee

2, 3, 4 and 5
Students' own answers.

6
Across: 3 Sardinia   6 gardening   7 temperature
8 centenarian   10 sleepy
Down: 1 advice   2 medicine   4 rate   5 Okinawa
9 nap

Unit 2
2a (pages 12 and 13)

1
1 T   2 F   3 T   4 T   5 T   6 F   7 F   8 T

2
1 surfing   2 rowing   3 kneel   4 oars   5 waves
6 athletic

3
1 have to   2 can   3 mustn't/can't   4 have to   5 can
6 must/have to

4
1 mustn't   2 don't   3 can   4 must   5 can't

5
1 Basketball: Each team has to / must have five players on
   the court.
2 Football: Players can't / mustn't get a red card.
3 Rugby: The referee can stop the match.
4 Running: You don't have to use any special equipment.
5 Tennis: The ball has to / must go over the net.

6
1 championship   2 Winners   3 score   4 line   5 referee
6 team   7 rules   8 spectators

2b (pages 14 and 15)

1
1 the World Cup
2 famous teams, local teams, school teams
3 over fifty
4 It's a good way to keep fit, it can help them live longer.
5 Players have to walk with the ball and have to keep one
   foot on the ground.
6 It's very slow.
7 Over 800

2a
a love   b really like   c enjoy   d don't mind
e don't like   f hate, can't stand

2b
Students' own answers.

3
1 Playing   2 Competing   3 cycling   4 Learning
5 losing   6 Sitting   7 being   8 flying
9 becoming   10 watching

4a
1 watching   2 language   3 waiting   4 thinks   5 cycling
6 losing   7 winning   8 English   9 competing   10 thanks

5
1 loves skiing all over the world
2 She's good at other sports
3 doesn't like running or going to the gym
4 sports people compete in different sports
5 they don't normally do
6 the competition
7 she'd like to win

2c (page 16)

1
1 b   2 c   3 d   4 a

2
1 c   2 b   3 c   4 a   5 c

3
1 e   2 f   3 c   4 d   5 g   6 a   7 b

4
1 'd like to play tennis later / feel like playing tennis later
2 look like someone
3 'd like to play
4 'd like some ice cream
5 isn't like

2d (page 17)

1
1 A 2 A 3 B 4 C 5 C 6 A 7 A

2
1 Boot Camp 2 Zumba 3 Pilates

3
1 interested in 2 not very 3 sounds good
4 we should 5 What about 6 Go on 7 I'd prefer
8 it looks

4
Model answers:
No, I wouldn't like to do it.
I hate getting up early.
I'm not very good at dancing.
Yes, I'd prefer that to Boot Camp or Zumba.

2e (page 18)

1
Possible answer:

> **COME JOIN THE FUN AFTER WORK THIS WEEK!**
> - **Where?** In the park
> - **What?** A barbecue with a 'fun' football match afterwards
> - **When?** Friday at six
> - **Why?** It's a great chance to meet some of your colleagues out of the office and really get to know each other.
>
> Please confirm by emailing me on r_shaw@shaw.com

2
1 capital letter 2 full stop, exclamation mark 3 comma
4 apostrophe

3
1 I (capital letter) 2 ✓ 3 gaming, cycling (comma)
4 It's (apostrophe) 5 ✓ 6 Canada (capital letter)
7 Saturday (capital letter) 8 ✓ 9 month. We (full
stop) 10 win. (full stop) / win! (exclamation mark)

Wordbuilding / Learning skills (page 19)

1
1 golfer 2 cyclist 3 swimmer 4 racing driver 5 athlete
6 runner

2
1 pronunciation 2 verb 3 present participle
4 past participle 5 definition 6 noun 7 plural form
8 first meaning 9 second meaning 10 main stress
11 adjective 12 example sentence

3
1 180 2 300 3 60 4 1.50 5 4 6 5 7 2 8 42

Unit 3

3a (pages 20 and 21)

1
a

2
1 T 2 F 3 F 4 T 5 F

3
1 rush hour 2 traffic jam 3 Fuel costs 4 public
transport 5 speed limit

4
more interesting, better, slower, the greenest, the most
rewarding, longer, much cheaper, more detailed, greener than

5
1 cheaper, cheapest 2 angrier, angriest 3 larger, largest
4 bigger, biggest 5 safer, safest 6 funnier, funniest
7 thinner, thinnest 8 lower, lowest 9 easier, easiest
10 greener, greenest 11 fitter, fittest 12 faster, fastest

6
Possible answers:
1 travelling by bus is more relaxing than travelling by car
2 cake is tastier than bread.
3 email is faster than letters.
4 teachers work harder than politicians.
5 aeroplanes are worse for the environment than trains.

7
1 tallest 2 smallest 3 fastest 4 longest 5 most dangerous
6 largest

8
1 <u>Your car</u> is <u>faster</u> than <u>mine</u>.
2 <u>Bicycles</u> are the <u>greenest</u> <u>transport</u>.
3 <u>Walking</u> is <u>slower</u> than <u>cycling</u>.
4 <u>Trains</u> are <u>cheaper</u> than <u>planes</u>.
5 <u>Hybrid</u> transport is the <u>most efficient</u>.

3b (pages 22 and 23)

1
1 Because they can walk further across deserts than any
  other kind of animal.
2 Carrying heavy loads, producing milk and meat.
3 No. People at the competition from countries like Oman,
  Saudi Arabia and Qatar think they are beautiful.
4 Ten days.
5 Around 24,000.
6 Rice, meat and the hump of the camel.

2
1 Horses are as good as modern transport in the forest.
2 The weather is always as hot as this in my country.
3 Silver isn't as expensive as gold.
4 New cars aren't as stylish as cars from the sixties.
5 Bicycles are as fast as cars in the city centre.
6 I'm not as young as I used to be.

4
1 d 2 b 3 a 4 c

5
1 as there was a traffic jam 2 You look as
3 a bicycle is as 4 as we drove home

6
1 frequent 2 punctual 3 traditional 4 convenient
5 reliable 6 comfortable

7
1 a bit 2 much 3 a little 4 a lot 5 a little 6 a bit
7 much 8 a bit

8
1 a lot / much higher 2 a lot / much more popular
3 a little / a bit lower 4 a little / a bit less popular

3c (page 24)

1
1 d 2 b 3 c 4 a

2
1 c 2 b 3 b 4 a 5 b

3
1 pick up   2 catch   3 go by   4 miss   5 go in   6 go

4
/æ/ catch, jam, plan, rank, taxi
/eɪ/ change, day, gate, plane, take, train

3d (page 25)

1
1 fare   2 rank   3 stop   4 receipt   5 gate   6 platform
7 check in   8 book

2
1 b   2 c   3 d   4 a

3
1 Outside the cinema.   2 A return ticket.   3 €20.50
4 At five fifteen.   5 Platform twelve.   6 Two bags.
7 £10   8 Yes.   9 Because it can't stop at a bus stop.
10 $13.30

4
1 Do you go   2 Can I have   3 I'd like a
4 Which platform   5 How many   6 Can I pay
7 How much   8 Have you got

5
1 Return, please.
2 Yes, this one.
3 No, with cash.
4 Yes, I do. Here you are.
5 Platform nine.

3e (page 26)

1
Message one: Get on the number 68 bus from the bus stop outside your house. Take it to the underground station. Catch the first train and get off at Oxford Road station. Then call me. I'll come and get you.

Message two: My flight is late and I'm still in Berlin. Don't wait for me at the airport. I'll catch the bus to the city centre and walk to your house. See you later.

Message three: Chris wants to meet us tonight, so please can you call him and tell him where to meet us? And send me the address of the restaurant as well. What time do you want to meet?

2
Possible answers:
Message one: Get 68 bus outside house to underground. Catch train to Oxford Road. Call. I'll get you.
Message two: Flight late. Still in Berlin. Don't wait. Will catch bus to yours.
Message three: Chris meeting us too. Tell him and me restaurant address and meeting time.

Wordbuilding / Learning skills (page 27)

1
1 credit   2 time   3 centre   4 transport   5 snow
6 driver   7 town   8 seat

2
1 alarm clock   2 bank account   3 boxing gloves
4 football pitch   5 letter box   6 mobile phone
7 tennis court   8 town centre

3 and 4
Students' own answers.

5
1 sledge   2 Kolkata   3 Iditarod   4 rank   5 luggage
6 adjective

Unit 4
4a (pages 28 and 29)

1
1 take risks   2 adventure   3 dangerous   4 my biggest achievement   5 a big challenge   6 ambition   7 crazy

2
1 visited   2 arrived   3 dried   4 stayed   5 jogged   6 lived
7 studied   8 moved

3
1 was born   2 studied   3 became   4 went   5 started
6 survived   7 grew up   8 played   9 learned   10 joined

4
1 F (Eskil was born in Norway.)
2 F (Brady studied at university.)
3 T
4 F (Eskil joined a circus.)
5 T
6 F (A python attacked Brady on his TV show.)
7 F (Eskil started performing on his own after he left the circus.)
8 T

5
1 When were you
2 did you grow up
3 did you study at university
4 did you learn
5 When did you join
6 When did you start

6a
1 bit   2 bought   3 hit   4 did   5 said   6 went
7 fought   8 brought   9 met

6b
/e/   said, went, met
/ɪ/   bit, hit, did
/ɔː/   bought, fought, brought

4b (pages 30 and 31)

1

				¹F				³P		⁴K		

Across: ²P A T I E N T

²P A T I E N T (row with ¹F R on top spelling FRIENDLY down)
⁵H A R D - W O R K I N G
⁶I N T E L L I G E N T
⁷E X P E R I E N C E D

2a
Across: 2 patient, 5 hard-working, 6 intelligent, 7 experienced
Down: 1 friendly, 3 positive, 4 kind

3
1 E   2 B   3 D   4 A   5 C, E   6 B, E   7 B   8 B, E

4
was changing, was flying, were climbing, was sailing

5
1 The sun was shining and people were sunbathing on the beach.
2 The phone was ringing, but I was leaving the house so I didn't answer it.
3 We weren't studying when the teacher walked in.
4 We were walking past the building when the fire started.
5 She wasn't thinking about her exam results when the envelope arrived.
6 It wasn't raining, so we went for a picnic.

6
1 Did you see   2 were following   3 saw
4 didn't hear   5 was listening   6 Did you have
7 didn't arrive   8 Were you waiting

7
1 c   2 b   3 e   4 a   5 d

8
1 fell in love   2 fell by 3%   3 fell off   4 fell asleep

4c (page 32)

1
1 e   2 c   3 a   4 g   5 c   6 b   7 d   8 f

2
Topics 2, 3, 4, 6

3
1 He led the team. / He was the team leader.
2 To find out if the tents could survive the difficult conditions in the rainforests.
3 Humans don't really need clothes in the rain forest.
4 Food and water.
5 He lost about twenty kilos.
6 Determination.

4
1 In   2 In   3 in   4 at   5 on   6 –   7 on   8 –   9 on

4d (page 33)

1
1 e   2 a   3 c   4 d   5 f   6 b

2
1 One day   2 after a few days   3 In the end
4 For some time   5 suddenly   6 While   7 luckily
8 Then   9 amazingly   10 after three weeks   11 Sadly

3
a One day, after a few days, after three weeks, For some time
b While, Then, In the end
c suddenly, amazingly
d luckily
e Sadly

4a
Speakers 1, 3 and 5

5
Model answers:
Why?
Oh no!
That was a good idea!
That was lucky!
Wow!

4e (page 34)

1a
1 C   2 A   3 E   4 B   5 D

1b
1 b   2 e   3 f   4 g   5 h   6 c   7 d   8 a

2b
1 We walked for three hours, and **then** we sat and enjoyed the view.
2 I arrived home **just** as the sun went down.
3 The explorers tried to leave their camp **again,** but the weather was still too bad.
4 After three hours we were **still** lost.
5 We were three days from anywhere, but we **only** had food and water for one more day.
6 The jungle is hot. **Also**, there are many dangerous animals.

3
Students' own answers.

Wordbuilding / Learning skills (page 35)

1
1 achievement   2 study   3 player   4 solution   5 answer
6 test   7 memory   8 score

2
1 test   2 solve   3 score   4 remember   5 play   6 achieve

3 and 4
Students' own answers.

5
1 and 2
Lukla: Pasang lived there, her parents died, she trained as a mountaineer, then there was an earthquake.
Kabul: Marjan Sadequi grew up there, she became a cyclist.
Tehran: Reza studied architecture there.
Siula Grande: Simpson and Yates climbed this mountain, but Simpson fell and broke his knee, then he fell over a cliff. Yates had to cut the rope. Simpson survived and made it back to the camp
Atafu: three boys went fishing, they were lost in the middle of the Pacific Ocean. But they were found and survived.

Unit 5

(pages 36 and 37)

1
Possible answers:
jar [C] – made of glass – for storing food
newspaper [C] – made of paper – for reading
aluminium foil [U] – made of metal – for wrapping food

2
1 a   2 some   3 a   4 a   5 an   6 some   7 some (also *a coffee* as in *a cup of coffee*)   8 a

3
1 jars   2 buses   3 countries   4 holidays   5 women
6 cans   7 boxes   8 children   9 phones   10 classes
11 stories   12 cartridges

4
1 a some, b any   2 a much, b some   3 a many, b any
4 a a lot of, b much   5 a a few, b a little   6 a many, b a few
7 a a little, b much

5
1 some   2 any   3 few   4 many   5 lot

6
1 d   2 b   3 a   4 e   5 c

7
1 Reusing them.
2 Old cotton shirts, old socks and old towels.
3 Glass jars, yoghurt pots and plastic containers.
4 Wrapping presents, protecting fragile objects, and compost.
5 Wrap old clothing around them.
6 Carrying shopping or putting bottles of liquid in when you travel.

5b (pages 38 and 39)

1

1 just over   2 well over   3 exactly   4 nearly

2

1 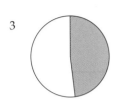   2

3 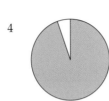   4

3

1 Australians   2 French   3 Indians
4 Chinese, Indians, Mexicans   5 Brazilians, Japanese
6 Chinese   7 Germans   8 Hungarians

4

1 B   2 C   3 A

5

1 40%   2 more people   3 cardboard   4 one day
5 glass bottles   6 about 1905, 51,000
7 London, 10,000 plants   8 plants and trees, air quality
9 noise and heat

6

1 –   2 the   3 –   4 The   5 a   6 the   7 –   8 the   9 an
10 –   11 the   12 the

7

/ðə/   Sentences 4, 8, 11 and 12
/ði:/   Sentences 2, 6

8

Over three hundred million people live in **the** United States of America. It is **the** world's most multi-cultural country. It was part of **the** United Kingdom but it became **a** new country in 1776. Washington DC became **the** capital city and the President still lives in **the** White House today. However, it isn't **the** biggest city. New York is **a** bigger city, and it's also more popular with tourists. In particular, they come to see **the** Statue of Liberty.

5c (page 40)

1

1 go by   2 go for   3 last   4 Slow down!   5 have
6 be careful   7 drink   8 carry

2

Students' own answers.

3

1 Environmental news
2 The USA
3 mobile phones, music players, laptops, computers, digital cameras
4 Yes (It can produce gold and reduce greenhouse gases.)
5 Paper recycling

4

1 243   2 82   3 24   4 32   5 17   6 3,500   7 150, 380   8 87

5d (page 41)

1

1 7786-P   2 £22   3 Bruce   4 31   5 Visa
6 4456 8938 9604 9500   7 bob.bruce51@email.com

2

1 d   2 c   3 f   4 h   5 b   6 a   7 g   8 e   9 i

3

Model answers
Yes, I'd like to order a laptop.
It's GR897-01
[Student's name]
Mastercard, please
7558 6799 3647 1023
Yes please
[Student's own email address]

5e (page 42)

1

1 d   2 b   3 c   4 f   5 e   6 g   7 h   8 a

2

1 would like … inform   2 'd be delighted   3 receive
4 request   5 apologize   6 provide   7 refund
8 require … assistance

3

1 Could you send me information about a DVD called '…'?
2 I'd like to know the price.
3 Please send me details as soon as possible.
4 Thank you for your interest in our products.
5 The price of this DVD is $10.
6 This includes delivery.
7 Thank you for your immediate reply.
8 I would like to order the DVD.
9 Please send me information on how to pay.

Wordbuilding / Learning skills (page 43)

1

1 Please board the plane as we are ready for take-off.
2 There's some out-of-date chicken here, I'll have to throw it away.
3 A lot of people are pro-European.
4 Nearly three-quarters of the population regularly recycles glass.
5 I only use eco-friendly washing detergent.
6 Do you have an up-to-date bus timetable?
7 My birthday is on the thirty-first of January.
8 My wife's mother is my mother-in-law.
9 A marathon is a twenty-six mile run. That's forty-two kilometres.
10 All our products use state-of-the-art technology.

2

Students' own answers.

3

1 uncountable: there is a U in brackets after 'noun'.
2 *foot* and *tooth* are countable, *information, luggage* and *time* are uncountable. *Time* can also be countable when it means 'occasion' or 'time on the clock', e.g. *I remember the time when …, What's the time now?*
3-5, Students' own answers.

4

1 Nearly thirty percent of the land on Earth is desert.
2 Computers use gold inside them.
3 They have the same meaning, but we use *a few* with countable nouns and *a little* with uncountable nouns.
4 They have the same meaning but 'tell' is less formal and more commonly used than the word 'inform'.
5 The Great Wall of China is a famous old wall, but the Green Wall is a wall of trees. The Chinese started planting it in 1978.
6 The Plastiki was made with plastic bottles.
7 The Pacific Ocean has an area called the Great Garbage Patch.
8 Something that is toxic is poisonous.
9 The African green wall will go from Senegal to Djibouti.
10 The Atacama desert is in Chile.

Unit 6

6a (pages 44 and 45)

1
1 go to university 2 leave home 3 buy their first home
4 get my driving licence 5 retire from work 6 start a family

2
1 B 2 D 3 A 4 C

3
1 Locally – perhaps in the nicer neighbourhoods.
2 He had visited the Palau islands many times.
3 About 7,500 kilometres west.
4 Green forests, interesting wildlife and a blue ocean full of colourful fish.
5 150
6 The head of the island.
7 $100
8 A free holiday by the beach.
9 The head of the island.

4
However, one day they ... decided to leave it all behind.

But actually, they planned to find a place in paradise to create their new home.

For Alex, it was fairly easy to choose an island with everything he wanted.

He continued to go back there from time to time, so this seemed like a good choice.

The islands are ... difficult to reach.

Before Alex and Sarah could start to work on building a house, they had to get permission from the head of the island – an 83-year-old woman.

She was worried they intended to develop the area for other tourists, but Alex explained that they just wanted to build a simple house.

Alex and Sarah didn't want to pay for a construction company, so they taught themselves a lot about building.

A lot of their friends from Iowa came out to help.

5
1 d 2 b 3 f 4 a 5 e 6 c 7 h 8 g

6
1 nice to see 2 difficult to keep 3 sad to see
4 afraid to move 5 easy to make 6 great to live

7
1 to help 2 throw 3 to meet 4 playing 5 going
6 to get

9
Students' own answers.

6b (pages 46 and 47)

1
1 parades 2 floats 3 masks / costumes
4 masks / costumes 5 fireworks 6 candles 7 bands

2
1 c 2 b 3 a 4 c

3
1 Because they want to discuss a surprise leaving party for Rosemary.
2 Because it isn't a good place to have fun.
3 It's next door and it's good.
4 Pizzas and Italian food.
5 About 20.
6 Between five and six.
7 The person is working late.
8 She loves plants and is going to do lots of gardening when she retires.
9 Because Rosemary is coming back from lunch.

4
1 is everyone going to meet
2 I'm working
3 are we going to give
4 she's going to spend
5 Will the restaurant make
6 I'll ask

5
1 a 2 b 3 b 4 b 5 a

6
1 a 2 b 3 b 4 a 5 b 6 a

7
1 ✓ 2 ✗ 3 ✗ 4 ✓ 5 ✗ 6 ✓ 7 ✗ 8 ✗

8
Tomorrow our town will be two hundred years old. We are going to have a huge celebration. We plan to have a street parade with costumes and masks. Local musicians are going to play traditional music and at midnight there are going to be fireworks!

6c (page 48)

1
1 d 2 c 3 b 4 a 5 e

2
1 4th July 2 girls 3 four 4 sun 5 child 6 ten
7 faces 8 women

3
1 up 2 back 3 ready 4 plane 5 presents 6 pension
7 married

6d (page 49)

1
1 On holiday. 2 After work. 3 Outside Sonia's office.
4 A friend from France. 5 Go into his lesson.
6 He has an exam tomorrow. 7 They could get home early or he could study first. 8 No.

2
1 Do you want 2 Yes, OK 3 How about 4 It sounds
5 Why don't you 6 That would 7 I'd like
8 It's very nice 9 I'd love to

3
Model answers:
Invitation 1
Sorry, I can't because I'm going to a football match tonight.
OK. That'd be great.

Invitation 2
It's very nice of you to ask, but isn't it only for your friend's family and close friends?
OK. I'd like that very much. Thank you.

4a
1 Speaker 1 2 Speaker 1 3 Speaker 2 4 Speaker 2
5 Speaker 1

6e (page 50)

1a
1 tasty 2 colourful 3 dull 4 massive 5 miserable
6 exciting

1b
1 b   2 a   3 e   4 f   5 c   6 d

1c
Possible answers:
a amazing, beautiful, dull, enormous, fun, pretty, smart, uncomfortable
b amazing, delicious, dull, unhealthy, enormous
c fun, amazing, attractive, smart, dull, unhealthy, enormous, miserable, friendly, beautiful
d amazing, polluted, speedy
e fun, amazing, enormous, friendly, beautiful
f amazing, enormous, beautiful

1d
Possible answers:
a scruffy clothes   b huge meals   c energetic people
d busy transport and towns   e international festivals
f stunning nature and geographic features

2
Model answer:
Our town festival is once a year at the end of August. It's always great fun because there are lots of different events. For example there are parades for children with colourful costumes. Then in the evening there is a big party with dancing and food. The food is always delicious. Lots of local shops sell food and you can try some of our traditional dishes. But my favourite part of the whole event is at midnight when there are lots of fireworks. They light the whole night sky up, and then it's time to go home.

3
Students' own answers.

Wordbuilding / Learning skills (page 51)

1
1 afraid   2 warm   3 awful   4 strong   5 tall   6 polite
7 hide   8 touch   9 needy   10 relaxed

2
Students' own answers.

3
A place: Port-of-Spain, Tremé
Type of dish or something you can eat: feijoada
Something that gives light: firework, candle
Stage of life: infant, middle-aged
A group of people: Hamar, teenagers

Unit 7

7a (pages 52 and 53)

1
1 have been   2 have spent   3 has created
4 has become   5 hasn't survived   6 was   7 were
8 made   9 didn't have   10 have disappeared

2
1 have oil companies been in the area
2 have they spent in the last decade
3 has the industry created
4 was Jim Boucher a child here
5 did people make a living
6 Did the area have

3
Person 1: I've lived here for five years. I moved here to work for the oil company. I think it's been good for the area. Before, there was nothing here. Now lots of people have moved here and they've built new towns.

Person 2: I've always lived in this area. It was a beautiful place, but then the oil companies came here. In my opinion they've polluted the rivers and have changed the area forever.

4
/ɔː/	bought, brought, taught, thought
/ʌ/	come, done, run, won
/əʊ/	flown, grown
/aʊ/	found

5
1 receptionist   2 sales representative
3 shop assistant   4 fashion designer
5 computer programmer   6 police officer
7 marketing manager

6
1 dangerous   2 boring   3 skilled   4 physical
5 challenging

7
1 've taught, for
2 haven't flown, since
3 has run, for
4 have grown, since
5 haven't seen, for
6 has lived, since

8
1 have you lived
2 have you known
3 have you had
4 have you been
Students' own answers.

9
1 been   2 gone   3 been   4 gone   5 been

7b (pages 54 and 55)

1
1 landscape architect   2 environmental cartoonist
3 in the garden

2
1 When he was a child.
2 He/She designs areas outside with trees and flowers.
3 It's creative and highly-skilled.
4 He thinks about his next cartoon.
5 She helps with ideas for the dialogues.
6 When he has lots of ideas.
7 a book award

3
1 down   2 in   3 opposite   4 on   5 next   6 across
7 through   8 up

4a
1 Go /w/ up the steps.
2 no /w/
3 no /w/
4 Sue /w/ often works on the third floor.
5 You /w/ are on the fifth floor today.
6 no /w/
7 Go /w/ in the lift.
8 no /w/
9 Go /w/ out of this door.

Answer key

5

Crossword answers: ²BASEMENT, ¹CANTEEN, ³GROUND, ⁴OFFICE, ⁵ENTRANCE, ⁶EXIT, ⁷STAIRS, ⁸LIFT, ⁹CORRIDOR

7c (page 56)

1
1 promotion 2 salary 3 colleagues 4 opportunities 5 pension 6 training

2
Person 1: c   Person 2: e   Person 3: f   Person 4: a   Person 5: b

3
1 Everyone in the village   2 Computer programs
3 Upstairs in the marketing department
4 Twenty years   5 Lots of training

4
make: a call, a mistake, a noise, coffee, dinner, money, your bed
do: a job, business, housework, well, work

5
1 money, make   2 make, a noise   3 do, housework
4 do, well   5 make, coffee   6 make, your bed
7 make, call   8 do, job

7d (page 57)

1
1 staff 2 description 3 provide 4 essential 5 position
6 apply 7 contact details / CV 8 contact details / CV

2
1 Her CV and letter of application.
2 receptionist
3 She works at the front desk in a hotel.
4 Welcoming people, answering the phone and dealing with any problems.
5 She's more interested in the interviewer's business.
6 She helped with organizing a conference.
7 She works hard, enjoys working with other people and she can solve problems.
8 training

3
1 g   2 e   3 a   4 c   5 d   6 b   7 f

4a
Students' own answers.

4b
Model answers:
1 I've been there since 2008.
2 I suppose so. I like hard work and I'd like to become successful in my career.
3 I enjoy working in a team. I think I'm good with other people.
4 Sometimes I work too hard. I don't know when to stop.
5 Once, I was in charge of some colleagues and it was difficult to tell them what to do.
6 As I said before, I like working in teams and I think people like working with me.
7 Let me think. Well, once we had a customer. She wasn't happy with the service and I had to deal with the problem.

7e (page 58)

1
1 Nationality   2 Date of birth   3 Address   4 Education
5 Work experience   6 Skills   7 Interests   8 Reference

2a
1 Taught   2 Advised   3 Designed   4 Welcomed
5 Looked after   6 Managed   7 Sold   8 Translated
9 Played   10 Assisted

2b
Education
1 studying Geography at University
2 learning English at a language school

Hobbies and interests
3 played in two football teams
4 play the Saxophone

Work experience
5 worked in a café at weekends
6 managed a group of teenagers on a summer camp

Wordbuilding / Learning skills (page 59)

1
1 librarian   2 actor   3 musician   4 photographer
5 accountant   6 writer   7 electrician   8 receptionist
9 employee / employer   10 manager   11 student   12 painter

2
1 ✗   2 ✓   3 ✗   4 ✗   5 ✓   6 ✓   7 ✓   8 ✗   9 ✓   10 ✗
11 ✓   12 ✓

3
1 waiter / waitress   2 artist   3 bank manager
4 geologist / geology student   5 ballet dancer   6 pianist

5
1 CV   2 do   3 won   4 BSc   5 on   6 X-ray
Job: cowboy

Unit 8
8a (pages 60 and 61)

1
1 download   2 log in to   3 subscribe to   4 search
5 write   6 set up   7 connect to   8 do

2
1 The GPS
2 It has a problem getting a signal when it rains.
3 A place for the helicopter to pick them up.
4 Two days away.
5 There are too many trees.
6 The battery.

3
1 it always has a problem.
2 if you want our location,
3 Press it again
4 he won't find anywhere to land
5 If we walk all day tomorrow
6 if the weather's good
7 we'll try to leave the day after

135

4

If it's raining, it always has a problem.
… if you want our location, press the button with a star.
Press it again if you want a closer view.
… if he flies closer to us, he won't find anywhere to land.
If we walk all day tomorrow, we might get there by the evening.
If the weather's good. If it isn't, then we'll try to leave the day after.

5

1 rains   2 I'll be amazed   3 connect   4 we'll leave
5 He usually texts   6 don't   7 don't   8 will

6a

1 ✗   2 ✗   3 ✓   4 ✓   5 ✗   6 ✓

6b

1 If   2 If   3 when   4 unless   5 unless

7

Possible answers:
If we don't take a camera, we can't take photos.
If we don't take a satnav we can't find our location.
If we don't take an umbrella, we can't stay dry.
If we don't take a torch, we can't see in the dark.
If we don't take matches, we can't light a fire.
If we don't take a cooker, we can't make a hot meal.

8b (pages 62 and 63)

1

1 invention   2 communicate   3 experiment   4 solve
5 instruction   6 decide

2

1 invent (2), invention (3)   2 communicate (4),
communication (5)   3 experiment (4), experiment (4)
4 solve (1), solution (3)   5 instruct (2), instruction (3)
6 decide (2), decision (3)

3

1 have   2 solve   3 follow   4 do   5 find   6 invent
7 make   8 get

4

b

5

1 An inventor.   2 Over fifty years ago.
3 Volvo.   4 No, not for many years.   5 Many governments
made laws that forced drivers to wear the seat belt.

6

which have changed our lives
which we don't notice and we don't know who invented them
who invented the modern-day car seatbelt
who worked for the car manufacturer Volvo
which went across the chest and across the legs and then joined at the same place
which no one had tried before
where it had the most customers
which had the invention

7

1 b   2 e   3 a   4 c   5 d

8

1 which changes with the sun
2 where the sun shines brightly
3 who works in a hot office
4 where there is less sunlight
5 who invented the windows

8c (page 64)

1

1 b   2 a   3 d   4 e   5 f   6 c   7 h   8 g

2

1 b   2 e   3 c   4 a   5 d

3

1 eyes and hair   2 ways of walking or moving
3 in security   4 if you lose your identity card, passport
or credit card   5 finger print, eyes   6 expensive
7 sometimes it makes mistakes   8 cheaper and more
effective, so it will become more and more important in our
everyday lives.

4

1 d   2 b   3 c   4 a   5 f   6 e

5

1 check in   2 checks   3 security check   4 check out
5 check for

8d (page 65)

1

1 the button   2 backwards   3 the battery   4 red button
5 forwards

2

Conversation 1: helmetcam
Conversation 2: GPS

3

a What is this for?
b Why do you need to do that?
c How do you switch it off?
d How long does the battery last?
e How did you do that?
f How does it work?
g Where do I switch it on?
h What happens if I press this other button?

4

1 a   2 f   3 g   4 d   5 e   6 h   7 b   8 c

5

1 How does‿it work?
2 This bit goes‿on your belt.
3 You can take‿it.
4 Let me have‿a look.
5 I can press this‿as well.

6

Model answers:
1 Really? How does it work?
2 I see.
3 That's very cool.
4 Let me have a look.

8e (page 66)

1

Paragraph 1: 1 b   2 a   3 d   4 e   5 c   6 f
Paragraph 2: 1 k   2 g   3 h   4 i   5 j

2

1 Firstly   2 For   3 In addition   4 In   5 Finally   6 As

3

1 c   2 e   3 g   4 b   5 d   6 a   7 f

4

Model answer:

Firstly, you can find any kind of information using a search engine. You type in a word and it will find lots of information about it. Secondly, you can find information in only a few seconds, so it's a very fast way of doing research. In addition, we can find information we need for everyday life, such as train times or the weather for the next week. In other words, it's a valuable source of information for work and studies.

Wordbuilding / Learning skills (page 67)

1

1 f   2 a   3 g   4 c   5 b   6 h   7 d   8 e

2

1 a about	b of
2 a about	b with
3 a with	b at
4 a about	b to
5 a with	b of

3

verb + preposition: *think of, think about, talk about, talk to*
adjective + preposition: *good at, good with, annoyed with, annoyed about*
noun + preposition: *problem with, problem of*

4 and 5

Students' own answers.

6

1 biomimetics   2 velcro   3 LED   4 Robonaut 2 or R2
5 Joshua Silver   6 GPS

Unit 9

9a (pages 68 and 69)

1

1 It had looked great in the brochure.
2 There'd been a delay on the motorway.
3 It was full of furniture, books, pictures and objects in boxes.
4 She thought she heard someone in the house.
5 clothes
6 The clothes were back in the wardrobe.
7 the owner of the cottage
8 The owner asked them not to move his clothes because he needed to use the house from time to time.

2

Paragraph 1: in the brochure; the sea, empty beaches
Paragraph 2: a six-hour drive
Paragraph 3: I woke up once; there were clothes in her wardrobe
Paragraph 4: the clothes were back in the wardrobe; My daughter's clothes were in the box on top of the wardrobe.
Paragraph 5: In the evening, as it got darker; lived in his shed when visitors stayed; The next day, we loaded the car and left.

3

1 e   2 b   3 d   4 f   5 c   6 a

4

1 b   2 a   3 e   4 c   5 d   6 f

5

1 book a tour
2 visit the pyramids
3 stay at comfortable hotels
4 rent a bicycle
5 go sightseeing
6 buy tickets

6

1 had been   2 had seen   3 hadn't imagined
4 had driven   5 had arrived   6 hadn't expected

7

1 Had you ever been   2 wasn't   3 had left
4 did that happen   5 He'd wanted   6 I received
7 had broken   8 gave

8

2 Contractions not possible
3 The hotel **didn't** have our reservation.
4 They **hadn't** eaten since they left home in the morning.
5 **I'd** lost my wallet so I called the police.
6 **You'd** left a message on my phone but you **hadn't** said where you were.

9b (pages 70 and 71)

1

1 c   2 e   3 f   4 a   5 d

2

a 3   b 5   c 4   d 1 and 2   e 4   f 5   g 1   h 2

3

1 amazing time with
2 the middle of
3 a fascinating place
4 were a bit worried
5 was tired
6 was exciting because
7 was a bit frightened on
8 was surprised because

4

●	tire, tired
●●	amaze, amazed, excite, surprise, surprised
●●	frighten, frightening, frightened, worry, worried, interest, tiring
●●●	amazing, exciting, excited, surprising
●●●	fascinate, interesting, interested, worrying
●●●●	fascinating, fascinated

5

1 Who showed
2 Where did
3 Who plays
4 What came
5 Where did
6 did they go
7 Who drove
8 Who met

6

1 d   2 g   3 e   4 h   5 b   6 a   7 f   8 c

7

1 S   2 O   3 S   4 S   5 O   6 O   7 S   8 S

9c (page 72)

1

1 b   2 a   3 c   4 a   5 c

2

The USA or Canada: 20% is normal, 10% if you don't get good service.
Central and South America: 10% is normal
Europe: 10% is normal
China or Japan: It isn't common to tip.
India and internationally: In many countries there is a service charge added so you don't need to tip.

3

1 cinema   2 museum   3 catacombs   4 gallery   5 theatre
6 tunnels

4
1 take place
2 a good place
3 all over the place
4 no place for

9d (page 73)

1

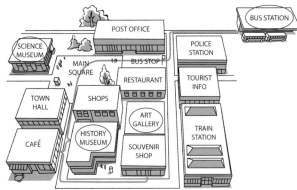

2
1 I'm interested in
2 Do you know
3 What time does
4 Could you tell
5 Are there any
6 How about
7 How much
8 You can also take
9 Is there any
10 Another option is

5
Model answers:
MA: I'm interested in visiting the city castle. Do you know
     the opening times?
MA: Great. Could you tell me the price?
MA: Is there a bus?
MA: How often does it leave?

9e (page 74)

1
1 a   2 c   3 g   4 d   5 f   6 h   7 i   8 e   9 j   10 b

2
1 b   2 a   3 b   4 b   5 a   6 c   7 b   8 c

Wordbuilding / Learning skills (page 75)

1
1 a amazing, b amazed
2 a fascinated, b fascinating
3 a interested, b interesting
4 a frightening, b frightened
5 a worried, b worrying
6 a tired, b tiring
7 a excited, b exciting
8 a surprising, b surprised

2
Students' own answers.

3
1 Let's stay at this hotel.
2 I'd like to book/buy two tickets for the tour.
3 I hadn't seen my friend for a long time.
4 Who lived in this house?
5 This is a good place to eat.

6 I'm interested in the museum.
7 Could you tell me the opening times?

5
1 abroad   2 tip   3 Tarxien   4 catacombs   5 gondola
6 Lascaux

Unit 10

10a (pages 76 and 77)

1
1 g   2 a   3 b   4 c   5 e   6 d   7 f

2
1 logo   2 customer   3 discount   4 marketing   5 advert
6 sales   7 poster

3
1 c   2 b   3 d   4 a

4
1 T   2 F   3 F   4 T   5 F   6 F   7 T

5
1 is made   2 are transported   3 are worn   4 is recognized
5 are sold   6 are advertised   7 are spent   8 is visited

6
1 The first bottle of Coca-Cola was made by John Pemberton
  in 1892.
2 The first email was sent by Ray Tomlinson in 1971.
3 The first Harry Potter book was written by JK Rowling
  in 1997.
4 The first plane was flown by the Wright brothers in 1903.
5 The first commercial film was shown by Louis and
  Auguste Lumiere in Paris in 1895.

7
1 recognize   2 are sold   3 is made   4 were called
5 changed   6 are taken   7 says   8 was chosen

8
1 was grown by the
2 was produced to make boats, baskets, boxes, tables,
3 was most famous as a
4 was cut into
5 pieces were put
6 is rarely made from papyrus
7 the plant is still used in

10b (pages 78 and 79)

1
1 a basic   b up-to-date
2 a fashionable   b old fashioned
3 a out-of-date   b classic
4 a useless   b useful

2
1 to connect with us through the internet
2 it lets humans 'talk' to their devices
3 They can text you.
4 You can switch the heating on when you are going home,
  or switch it off after you leave.
5 Because employers can check when workers are at their
  desk and when they aren't.
6 To check their health and measure their physical exercise.
7 From the data their devices collect about them.
8 When you are in and when you are out of the house.

3
1 use to   2 used to   3 used to   4 used to   5 worked
6 became   7 used to   8 used

4
1 used to love
2 Did you use to have
3 didn't use to take
4 used to ride
5 never used to work
6 Did they use to know
7 didn't use to let
8 did you use to pay

6
1 My sister didn't use to be interested in business when she was a student.
2 not possible
3 not possible
4 My family used to record music on tape cassettes.
5 Before I had a car, I used to cycle everywhere and I was / used to be much fitter!
6 not possible
7 My grandfather didn't use to pay for anything with a credit card.
8 Europeans didn't use to eat pasta before the thirteenth century.

10c (page 80)

1a
1 b   2 c   3 a

1b
1 b   2 a   3 c

1c
Stuff is uncountable, *thing* is countable

2
1 stuff   2 things / stuff   3 thing   4 stuff   5 thing /stuff
6 stuff

3
a 6   b 1   c 2   d 5   e 3   f 4

4
1 b   2 c   3 c   4 b   5 a   6 b

10d (page 81)

1

1	w	e	b	s	i	t	e		
2			c	o	n	t	e	n	t
3			c	o	n	t	a	c	t
4			a	d	v	e	r	t	s
5			s	e	a	r	c	h	
6				l	i	n	k	s	
7			h	o	m	e			
8		a	b	o	u	t			

2
1 a blog
2 because they like reading news
3 news about products, interviews with customers who use their products, and photos of employees in their free time
4 That Katarina writes the first post and they see if people read it.

3
1 What do you think   2 we should   3 in my opinion
4 I agree   5 I'm not sure   6 I see what   7 Maybe
8 we could   9 You're right

10e (page 82)

1
1 c   2 a   3 e   4 f   5 b   6 d   7 h   8 g

2
1 d   2 a   3 b   4 g   5 e   6 c   7 f

3
One of my favourite apps is Starfinder. It's a great app for looking at stars at night and recognizing them.
The app has quite a few different features. Firstly, it gives you lots of information about the star when it sees one. Another good point is that it gives you links to websites with more information.
The only problem with the app is that if you move your phone too quickly it can give the wrong information.
On the whole, it's a useful app for anyone who is fascinated by the stars and the planets.

Wordbuilding / Learning skills (page 83)

1
1 advert   2 Advertising   3 advertise   4 productive
5 product   6 invention   7 inventor   8 sold   9 sale

2
O: sales, sell, sold
Oo: *advert*, product
oO: invent, produce
Ooo: advertise
oOo: production, productive, invention, inventor
Oooo: advertising
oOoo: advertisement

5 Example answers
1 The man in the photo makes baskets in his home in Hung Yen in Vietnam,
2 The first YouTube video was called 'Me at the zoo' and it was made by Jawed Karim.
3 On the first Apple laptops, the logo was upside down when the laptop was open.
4 Gap changed its famous blue logo in 2010, but then changed it back.
5 In 1986, *Walkman* was included as a word in the English dictionary.
6 The website called The Minimalists helps people to have less stuff, and has 2,000,000 visitors a month.

Unit 11

11a (pages 84 and 85)

1
1 B   2 C   3 F   4 A   5 E

2
1 1990; In a library; Someone was sending an email.
2 1945; (doesn't say where); There were parties and people celebrated.
3 1987; Outside a hotel; lines of people waiting, a lot of excitement, and the yellow symbol.
4 1969; At aunt and uncle's because they had a TV; Remembers the words, 'one giant leap for mankind.'
5 1989; In Germany; The speaker travelled across Europe to get a piece of the wall.

3
1 The astronaut thought, 'I hope this works.'
2 The climber shouted, 'Hello!'
3 'See me after class,' the teacher said to the student.
4 The customs officer asked, 'Can I see your passport, please?'
5 'Sorry, I've lost it,' replied the tourist.

4

1 could   2 was   3 showed   4 loved   5 would

5

2 'It's one small step for man, one giant leap for mankind.'
3 'The mission shows how the two countries can work together.'
4 'I love space!'
5 'The USA will send the first humans to Mars by 2030.'

6

1 He said that he wasn't interested in science.
2 They said that they were leaving early in the morning.
3 The girl shouted that she had found her purse.
4 My grandmother said that she had lived there when she had been a girl.
5 The scientist said that one day they would discover the solution.
6 The tourist said that he was lost.
7 The astronauts said that they had landed.

11b (pages 86 and 87)

1

1 c   2 b   3 c   4 b   5 c   6 a   7 a

2

1 b   2 a   3 d   4 e   5 c

3

1 T   2 F   3 F   4 T   5 F   6 F

4

1 say   2 tell   3 said   4 tell   5 told   6 said   7 told   8 said

5a

1 I love this video game.
2 Lizzie, I left a message on your phone.
3 We'll meet you later.
4 Peter, I'm sending you an email.
5 They've put a job advert in the newspaper.
6 Your picture is on Facebook, Sally.

5b

1 He said that he loved that video game.
2 She told Lizzie that she had left a message on her phone.
3 They said they would meet us later.
4 I told Peter I was sending him an email.
5 I told my manager that they had put a job advert in the newspaper.
6 He told Sally that her picture was on Facebook.

6

1 But you told me you had a <u>great</u> time!
2 But you told me you <u>loved</u> them!
3 No, I said I wanted to <u>watch</u> football.
4 But you said the tickets were <u>cheap</u>.
5 No, she told us that it happened in nineteen <u>eighty</u>-three.

11c (page 88)

1

1 statues   2 paintings   3 Archaeologists   4 robbers
5 pots   6 soldiers   7 tombs   8 collectors

2

1 Rio de Janeiro is one of Brazil's largest cities but it isn't the largest.
2 Normally the shop is busy but we've only had one or two people this morning.
3 Reinhold Messner is one person who has climbed Mount Everest.
4 I'd like to talk to you one by one, not as a group.
5 We plan to visit Egypt one day.

3

71 AD	c
9th century	e
11th century	d
1980s	b
Now	*a*

4

1 two   2 thousands   3 good places to eat   4 history
5 walls   6 Norway, Sweden   7 statues, pots (for cooking)
8 in the north   9 buildings

11d (page 89)

1

1 the first few days
2 the job
3 her journeys through the country and experiences of the culture
4 questions

2

1 l   2 b   3 j   4 f   5 d   6 h   7 c   8 e   9 a   10 g
11 k   12 i

3

Introducing the talk and the different parts: l, b, j, f, a, d
Ending a part of the presentation: h
Introducing the next part: c, e
Announcing the conclusion and ending: g, k, i

4

Hello and thank you for coming. / Today / I would like to talk about my gap year in Vietnam. / First / I'll describe my first few days there. / Then I'll move on to my job there / and I'll show you some of my photographs. / Finally, / I'll talk about my journeys through the country / and describe my experiences of the culture. / So let's begin …/

So that's everything I wanted to say about the first few days. / Now let's move on to the kind of work I was doing. / We'll take a look at this photo. / It shows you the school I worked in / and all the children … /

OK. / So the final part of my presentation is about my journeys. / I travelled a bit at weekends / but also I took a longer journey in the last month of my gap year. / So I'd like to show you some of my photos from that period / and I'll read a few comments from my diary… /

Right. / That's the end of my talk. / As you can see, / I had an amazing few months and, / to sum up, / I'd recommend it to anyone. / We have about ten minutes left / so are there any questions?

11e (page 90)

1

Tenzing Norgay is famous because, with the climber Edmund Hillary, he was the first man to reach the summit of Mount Everest on May 29, 1953. He was born in 1914 in a village called Thami near the border with Tibet. He spent most of his life in the region and worked on many expeditions to Everest before he reached the top. Afterwards, his life completely changed and he travelled all over the world. Before he died in 1986 he said about his life, 'It has been a long road.'

2

Possible answer:
Edmund Hillary was born in 1919 in Auckland, New Zealand. He began climbing in the Alps aged 16, but he is famous because, with Tenzing Norgay, he was the first man to reach the summit of Mount Everest. After climbing Everest

he spent a lot of time raising money to help local people in the Everest region. Before he died in 2008 he said about climbing, 'It is not the mountain we conquer but ourselves.'

Wordbuilding / Learning skills (page 91)

1
1 work on   2 pick up   3 play against   4 talk about
5 come out   6 think of

2
1 c   2 e   3 d   4 a   5 f   6 b

3 and 4
Students' own answers.

5
Possible answer:

The life of Reinhold Messner

1944: born in northern Italy. Father also a climber.

In his twenties: climbed with younger brother called Günther – died in accident.

1978: one of the first men to climb Everest without oxygen. First man to climb 14 mountains over 8,000 metres.

2006: opened museum.

Now: spends more time at home with family. Written sixty books.

6
1 the South Pole
2 1972
3 Scottish
4 the ancient Greeks
5 Busiris
6 the city of Machu Picchu
7 oxygen

Unit 12

12a (pages 92 and 93)

1
1 weather   2 tornado   3 flood   4 snowstorm   5 sun
6 thunderstorm

2
1 b   2 b   3 c   4 b   5 c   6 a

3
1 would happen if the fault opened
2 it opened and there was an earthquake, we'd probably fall over.
3 It'd be really difficult to stand up
4 we'd probably be safer
5 we knew this, we could make a much bigger difference

4
1 won   2 didn't   3 I'd go   4 had   5 I'd set up
6 wouldn't want   7 I'd give   8 I spent

6
1 If I saw a tornado, I'd run!
2 If she was more qualified, she'd get the job.
3 If it stopped raining, we'd go out.
4 If he had a car, he wouldn't take the bus.
5 If they knew the answer, they'd tell you.

12b (pages 94 and 95)

1

¹P	A	²R	K			³M		
		I				O		
⁴F		V				U		
I		E				N		
E		⁵F	⁶O	R	E	S	T	
L			C			A		
⁷D	E	S	E	R	T		I	
			A			N		
⁸G	A	R	D	E	N			

2
1 C   2 B   3 A   4 A   5 D   6 C   7 D   8 B   9 C   10 D

3
1 beaver   2 alligator   3 leopard   4 duck   5 turtle

4
1 anywhere   2 no one   3 somewhere   4 something
5 Everyone   6 nothing   7 Everywhere   8 anything
9 Everything   10 somebody

5
1 somewhere   2 anything   3 Everyone / Everybody
4 no one / nobody   5 everywhere   6 nothing
7 everywhere   8 Someone / Somebody

12c (page 96)

1
1 tool   2 discovery   3 habitat   4 survive   5 conservation
6 lecture

2
1 c   2 e   3 d   4 a   5 b

3
1 d   2 e   3 a   4 b   5 c

4
1 b   2 a   3 c   4 b   5 c

12d (page 97)

1
1 They are going to pull down all the old buildings and do something with the area.
2 The council doesn't have any money this year.
3 Selling the land for more housing.
4 Somewhere to relax.
5 Make it into a park.
6 Make a lake.
7 They don't have any money to pay professionals.
8 They will ask the local community for ideas and volunteers.

2
1 e   2 a   3 g   4 c   5 b   6 h   7 f   8 d

3
a 4   b 7   c 2   d 5   e 1   f 6   g 8   h 3

4
Model answers:
1 That's a good idea.
2 Sounds great!
3 I'm not sure.
4 No, that won't work.

12e (page 99)

1
1 a, d
2 b, c, g, i
3 e, f, h

2
1 1840
2 south-west London
3 for specialists who want to study and research plants
4 to educate people and to keep many species
   of different plants alive
5 100 attractions, including an art gallery
6 the Pagoda, which was built in 1762
7 the Treetop Walkway
8 to get children interested in trees
9 growing rare plants and flowers

Wordbuilding / Learning skills (page 99)

1
After a weekend of <u>violent</u> <u>storms</u>, the <u>good news</u> is that the country will return to normal. If you live in the north of the country, there will be some <u>heavy rain</u> through the night, but by morning this will disappear and you'll have a day of <u>bright sunshine</u>. You won't get any rain if you live further south, but expect some <u>strong winds</u> after midday. Other than that, you'll have a <u>beautiful day</u>.

2
1 storm   2 rain   3 wind   4 sun   5 park
6 attraction   7 climate   8 news

3
Student's own answers.

4
Possible answers:
1 snow / thunder   2 windscreen   3 anybody   4 tornado
5 If anyone else drove in that direction, they'd be mad.
6 comma   7 natural   8 Why don't we go to the cinema?

IELTS practice test

Listening

1 A   the hotel you're going to work at is actually called the Bristol.
2 C   So for the first few days you will help out in the manager's office
3 5/five   Yes, but it means working five hours a day, six days a week.
4 midday/noon/12.00   And during your stay, you'll do morning, <u>afternoon</u> and evening shifts. That means starting at either seven in the morning, <u>at midday</u> or at five in the evening. For the first week, <u>you'll be on the afternoon shift</u>.
5 Friday(s)   I've agreed that you'll be free on Fridays.
6 shared room   free accommodation is included – but that's in a shared room.
7 breakfast   Breakfast is provided free of charge in the hotel.
8 (hotel) shop   if you buy anything in the hotel shop, you get 10% off
9 (Mrs) D R I N K S T O N E
10 report   you'll be asked to write a report each week.
11 C   the main university campus … can be found just next door.
12 B   The majority … stay in host-family accommodation
13 A   students can use the football pitch without having to pay.
14 D/E   There's also a selection of English language films on DVD, which students can watch
15 E/D   got a selection of magazines, which is updated weekly,
16 morning(s)   fifteen-hour course … come to school in the morning only
17 12/twelve   There are twelve students in the class
18 465   this course costs £465 per week
19 Friday   with the exception of Friday
20 personal tutorial   each student has a personal tutorial once a week
21 Three/3   two days a week for … three weeks
22 (shopping) centre   I thought outside the shopping centre would be a good place
23 C   whilst one of us counts the cars, the other one can be in the car park doing the interviews … Let's take it in turns to do both these jobs
24 C   whilst one of us counts the cars, the other one can be in the car park doing the interviews … Let's take it in turns to do both these jobs
25 B   Adam: … prepare the questionnaire … would you mind doing that? Becky: I'd be happy to.
26 A   Becky: Then maybe you could save the data on to the laptop each day. Adam: OK, I think I could manage that.
27 A   we need to ask them why they chose to travel at that time
28 C   Adam: … ask them what they think about climate change … Becky: That's a good idea.
29 A   Adam: I think that writing the actual report is a job that's best done by one person. Becky: I'm happy to do that if you like. … If you want to do a draft though, for me to work from, that would be OK.
30 B   Adam: It will do me good to do it actually – give me more confidence about speaking in public.
31 cities / city streets   As cities became cleaner, there was less for the birds to eat
32 dirty   Some people even killed them because they thought they were dirty
33 eggs   it became a target for people who collected birds' eggs as a hobby
34 committee   1903, people interested in red kite conservation formed a committee.
35 Spain   the first reintroduced birds came from Spain and Sweden.
36 Ninety-three/93   a total of ninety-three birds being set free
37 Scotland   in 1996 a similar one began in Scotland
38 human   the birds must have disappeared due to human activity
39 habitat   there must still be a habitat which is suitable for the birds in the country.
40 genetically   must be similar genetically to the birds that used to live in the area

Reading

1 F   kitchen corner with microwave and sink
2 D   rent includes meals on a half-board basis
3 E   private shower and wc
4 F   free for two months in July and August
5 C   space for one bicycle in the (lockable) garden
6 B   wrongly delivered mail
7 E   weight and size guide
8 C   international parcels
9 E   restricted and prohibited goods
10 E   sending cash
11 A   compare sending options
12 B   redirection options
13 D   buy stamps online
14 E   wrapping and packaging
15 iv   You are coming to the UK for a limited period
16 v   You are coming to live in the UK for a longer period
17 iii   You must tell the DVLA about relevant conditions or disabilities that existed before you came to the UK
18 viii   You want to take a British driving test
19 ii   which are exempt from the normal large vehicle driver licensing requirements
20 vii   You drive a coach or lorry as your job
21 theory test   You cannot normally take the practical test without first having passed the theory test.
22 computerized touch screen   The first is a computerized touch screen test
23 video clips   You will be shown a set of video clips of driving hazards
24 40/forty minutes   and normally lasts 40 minutes
25 vehicle safety   The practical test also includes two questions on vehicle safety
26 photocard provisional licence   if you have a photocard provisional licence and your personal details have not changed, you can hand it over to the examiner,
27 driving offences   If during the probationary period, you are convicted of driving offences for which six or more penalty points are awarded, your driving licence will be revoked.
28 1887   a game was played that was very similar to the one we call badminton today
29 1893   A set of modern rules was drawn up and published in 1893
30 1895   and the Badminton Association of England was formed in 1895
31 1899   held in 1899 and 1900, for men and women respectively
32 1934   in 1934 an International Badminton Federation (IBF) was set up
33 1957   The first international women's championships were held in 1957.

34 1992   it was 1992 before badminton was played as a fully recognized Olympic sport

35 TRUE   although they were kicked rather than being hit with a racquet in those days.

36 FALSE   shuttlecocks were first used about 2,500 years ago in China

37 FALSE   in England. That's where a net was first introduced in 1867

38 FALSE   Badminton can be played by both men and women, although slightly different rules and scoring systems apply.

39 TRUE   Olympic sport – with the mixed doubles being added in 1996.

40 NOT GIVEN   It is one of the fastest racquet sports, with shuttlecocks travelling at up to 260 miles per hour